IDS 3920

UNIVERSITY COLLOQUIUM

A Sustainable Future

FLORIDA GULF COAST UNIVERSITY

Copley Custom Textbooks

An imprint of XanEdu Custom Publishing

ISBN 13: 978-1-58152-635-6
ISBN 10: 1-58152-635-0

Cover photo: Bob Klein.

Acknowledgments:

pp. 1–10: From *Experience and Education* by John Dewey. Copyright © 1938 by Kappa Delta Pi International Honor Society. Reprinted by permission of the rights holder via the Copyright Clearance Center.

pp. 11–27: From *Last Child in the Woods* by Richard Louv. Copyright © 2005 by Richard Louv. Reprinted by permission of Algonquin Books of Chapel Hill. All rights reserved.

pp. 28–41: From *A Sand County Almanac: With Essays on Conservation from Round River* by Aldo Leopold. Copyright © 1949 by Oxford University Press. Reprinted by permission of the publisher via the Copyright Clearance Center.

pp. 42–79: From *The Everglades: River of Grass* by Marjory Douglas Stoneham. Copyright © 1988 by Pineapple Press. Reprinted by permission of the publisher.

pp. 80–91: From *The Swamp* by Michael Grunwald. Copyright © 2006 by Michael Grunwald. All rights reserved. Reprinted with the permission of Simon & Schuster, Inc.

pp. 96–115: From *Ecological Literacy: Education and the Transition to a Postmodern World* by David W. Orr. Copyright © 1991 by State University of New York. All rights reserved. Reprinted by permission.

pp. 116–120: From *The Last Refuge: Patriotism, Politics, and the Environment in an Age of Terror* by David W. Orr. Copyright © 2004 by Island Press. Reprinted by permission of the publisher via the Copyright Clearance Center.

pp. 121–132: From *Earth in Mind: On Education, Environment, and the Human Prospect* by David W. Orr. Copyright © 2004 by Island Press. Reprinted by permission of the publisher via the Copyright Clearance Center.

pp. 133–138: As appeared in *The Humanist*, Volume 62, No. 2, 2003. Copyright © 2003 by American Humanist Association. Reprinted by permission of the publisher via the Copyright Clearance Center.

Contents

Traditional versus Progressive Education

John Dewey

MANKIND likes to think in terms of extreme opposites. It is given to formulating its beliefs in terms of *Either-Ors*, between which it recognizes no intermediate possibilities. When forced to recognize that the extremes cannot be acted upon, it is still inclined to hold that they are all right in theory but that when it comes to practical matters circumstances compel us to compromise. Educational philosophy is no exception. The history of educational theory is marked by opposition between the idea that education is development from within and that it is formation from without; that it is based upon natural endowments and that education is a process of overcoming natural inclination and substituting in its place habits acquired under external pressure.

At present, the opposition, so far as practical affairs of the school are concerned, tends to take the form of contrast between traditional and progressive education. If the underlying ideas of the former are formulated broadly, without the qualifications required for accurate statement, they are found to be about as follows: The subject-matter of education consists of bodies of information and of skills that have been worked out in the past; therefore, the chief business of the school is to transmit them to the new generation. In the past, there have also been developed standards and rules of conduct; moral training consists in forming habits of action in conformity with these rules and standards. Finally, the general pattern of school organization (by which I mean the relations of pupils to one another and to the teachers) constitutes the school a kind of institution sharply marked off from other social institutions. Call up in imagination the ordinary schoolroom, its time-schedules, schemes of classification, of examination and promotion, of rules of order, and I think you will grasp what is meant by "pattern of organization." If then you contrast this scene with what goes on in the family, for example, you will appreciate what is meant by the school being a kind of institution sharply marked off from any other form of social organization.

The three characteristics just mentioned fix the aims and methods of instruction and discipline. The main purpose or objective is to prepare the young for future responsibilities and for success in life, by means of acquisition of the organized bodies of information and prepared forms of skill which comprehend the material of instruction. Since the subject-matter as well as standards of proper conduct are handed down from the past, the attitude of pupils must, upon the whole, be one of docility, receptivity, and obedience. Books, especially textbooks, are the chief representatives of the lore and wisdom of the past, while teachers are the organs through which pupils are brought into effective connection with the material. Teachers are the agents through which knowledge and skills are communicated and rules of conduct enforced.

I have not made this brief summary for the purpose of criticizing the underlying philosophy. The rise of what is called new education and progressive schools is of itself a product of discontent with traditional education. In effect it is a criticism of the latter. When the implied criticism is made explicit it reads somewhat as follows: The traditional scheme is, in essence, one of imposition from above and from outside. It imposes adult standards, subject-matter, and methods upon those who are only growing slowly toward maturity. The gap is so great that the required subject-matter, the methods of learning and of behaving are foreign to the existing capacities of the young. They are beyond the reach of the experience the young learners already possess. Consequently, they must be imposed; even though good teachers will use devices of art to cover up the imposition so as to relieve it of obviously brutal features.

But the gulf between the mature or adult products and the experience and abilities of the young is so wide that the very situation forbids much active participation by pupils in the development of what is taught. Theirs is to do—and learn, as it was the part of the six hundred to do and die. Learning here means acquisition of what already is incorporated in books and in the heads of the elders. Moreover, that which is taught is thought of as essentially static. It is taught as a finished product, with little regard either to the ways in which it was originally built up or to changes that will surely occur in the future. It is to a large extent the cultural product of societies that assumed the future would be much like the past, and yet it is used as educational food in a society where change is the rule, not the exception.

If one attempts to formulate the philosophy of education implicit in the practices of the new education, we may, I think, discover certain common principles amid the variety of progressive schools now existing. To imposition from above is opposed expression and cultivation of individuality; to external discipline is opposed free activity; to learning from texts and teachers, learning through experience; to acquisition of isolated skills and techniques by drill, is opposed acquisition of them as means of attaining ends which make direct vital appeal; to preparation for a more or less remote future is opposed making

the most of the opportunities of present life; to static aims and materials is opposed acquaintance with a changing world.

Now, all principles by themselves are abstract. They become concrete only in the consequences which result from their application. Just because the principles set forth are so fundamental and far-reaching, everything depends upon the interpretation given them as they are put into practice in the school and the home. It is at this point that the reference made earlier to *Either-Or* philosophies becomes peculiarly pertinent. The general philosophy of the new education may be sound, and yet the difference in abstract principles will not decide the way in which the moral and intellectual preference involved shall be worked out in practice. There is always the danger in a new movement that in rejecting the aims and methods of that which it would supplant, it may develop its principles negatively rather than positively and constructively. Then it takes its clew in practice from that which is rejected instead of from the constructive development of its own philosophy.

I take it that the fundamental unity of the newer philosophy is found in the idea that there is an intimate and necessary relation between the processes of actual experience and education. If this be true, then a positive and constructive development of its own basic idea depends upon having a correct idea of experience. Take, for example, the question of organized subject-matter—which will be discussed in some detail later. The problem for progressive education is: What is the place and meaning of subject-matter and of organization *within* experience? How does subject-matter function? Is there anything inherent in experience which tends towards progressive organization of its contents? What results follow when the materials of experience are not progressively organized? A philosophy which proceeds on the basis of rejection, of sheer opposition, will neglect these questions. It will tend to suppose that because the old education was based on ready-made organization, therefore it suffices to reject the principle of organization *in toto*, instead of striving to discover what it means and how it is to be attained on the basis of experience. We might go through all the points of difference between the new and the old education and reach similar conclusions. When external control is rejected, the problem becomes that of finding the factors of control that are inherent within experience. When external authority is rejected, it does not follow that all authority should be rejected, but rather that there is need to search for a more effective source of authority. Because the older education imposed the knowledge, methods, and the rules of conduct of the mature person upon the young, it does not follow, except upon the basis of the extreme *Either-Or* philosophy, that the knowledge and skill of the mature person has no directive value for the experience of the immature. On the contrary, basing education upon personal experience may mean more multiplied and more intimate contacts between the mature and the immature than ever existed in the traditional school, and consequently more, rather than less, guidance by others. The problem, then, is: how these contacts can be established without violating the principle of learning through personal experience. The solution of this problem requires a well thought-out philosophy of the social factors that operate in the constitution of individual experience.

What is indicated in the foregoing remarks is that the general principles of the new education do not of themselves solve any of the problems of the actual or practical conduct and management of progressive schools. Rather, they set new problems which have to be worked out on the basis of a new philosophy of experience. The problems are not even recognized, to say nothing of being solved, when it is assumed that it suffices to reject the ideas and practices of the old education and then go to the opposite extreme. Yet I am sure that you will appreciate what is meant when I say that many of the newer schools tend to make little or nothing of organized subject-matter of study; to proceed as if any form of direction and guidance by adults were an invasion of individual freedom, and as if the idea that education should be concerned with the present and future meant that acquaintance with the past has little or no role to play in education. Without pressing these defects to the point of exaggeration, they at least illustrate what is meant by a theory and practice of education which proceeds negatively or by reaction against what has been current in education rather than by a positive and constructive development of purposes, methods, and subject-matter on the foundation of a theory of experience and its educational potentialities.

It is not too much to say that an educational philosophy which professes to be based on the idea of freedom may become as dogmatic as ever was the traditional education which is reacted against. For any theory and set of practices is dogmatic which is not based upon critical examination of its own underlying principles. Let us say that the new education emphasizes the freedom of the learner. Very well. A problem is now set. What does freedom mean and what are the conditions under which it is capable of realization? Let us say that the kind of external imposition which was so common in the traditional school limited rather than promoted the intellectual and moral development of the young. Again, very well. Recognition of this serious defect sets a problem. Just what is the role of the teacher and of books in promoting the educational development of the immature? Admit that traditional education employed as the subject-matter for study facts and ideas so bound up with the past as to give little help in dealing with the issues of the present and future. Very well. Now we have the problem of discovering the connection which actually exists *within* experience between the achievements of the past and the issues of the present. We have the problem of ascertaining how acquaintance with the past may be translated into a potent instrumentality for dealing effectively with the future. We may reject knowledge of the past as the *end* of education and thereby only emphasize its importance as a *means*. When we do that we have a problem that is new in the story of education: How shall the young become acquainted with the past in such a way that the acquaintance is a potent agent in appreciation of the living present?

The Need of a Theory of Experience

John Dewey

IN SHORT, the point I am making is that rejection of the philosophy and practice of traditional education sets a new type of difficult educational problem for those who believe in the new type of education. We shall operate blindly and in confusion until we recognize this fact; until we thoroughly appreciate that departure from the old solves no problems. What is said in the following pages is, accordingly, intended to indicate some of the main problems with which the newer education is confronted and to suggest the main lines along which their solution is to be sought. I assume that amid all uncertainties there is one permanent frame of reference: namely, the organic connection between education and personal experience; or, that the new philosophy of education is committed to some kind of empirical and experimental philosophy. But experience and experiment are not self-explanatory ideas. Rather, their meaning is part of the problem to be explored. To know the meaning of empiricism we need to understand what experience is.

The belief that all genuine education comes about through experience does not mean that all experiences are genuinely or equally educative. Experience and education cannot be directly equated to each other. For some experiences are mis-educative. Any experience is mis-educative that has the effect of arresting or distorting the growth of further experience. An experience may be such as to engender callousness; it may produce lack of sensitivity and of responsiveness. Then the possibilities of having richer experience in the future are restricted. Again, a given experience may increase a person's automatic skill in a particular direction and yet tend to land him in a groove or rut; the effect again is to narrow the field of further experience. An experience may be immediately enjoyable and yet promote the formation of a slack and careless attitude; this attitude then operates to modify the quality of subsequent experiences so as to prevent a person from getting out of them what they have to give. Again, experiences may be so disconnected from one another that, while each is agreeable or even exciting in itself, they are not linked cumulatively to one another. Energy is then dissipated and a person becomes scatterbrained. Each experience may be lively, vivid, and "interesting," and yet their disconnectedness may artificially generate dispersive, disintegrated, centrifugal habits. The consequence of formation of such habits is inability to control future experiences. They are then taken, either by way of enjoyment or of discontent and revolt, just as they come. Under such circumstances, it is idle to talk of self-control.

Traditional education offers a plethora of examples of experiences of the kinds just mentioned. It is a great mistake to suppose, even tacitly, that the traditional schoolroom was not a place in which pupils had experiences. Yet this is tacitly assumed when progressive education as a plan of learning by experience is placed in sharp opposition to the old. The proper line of attack is that the experiences which were had, by pupils and teachers alike, were largely of a wrong kind. How many students, for example, were rendered callous to ideas, and how many lost the impetus to learn because of the way in which learning was experienced by them? How many acquired special skills by means of automatic drill so that their power of judgment and capacity to act intelligently in new situations was limited? How many came to associate the learning process with ennui and boredom? How many found what they did learn so foreign to the situations of life outside the school as to give them no power of control over the latter? How many came to associate books with dull drudgery, so that they were "conditioned" to all but flashy reading matter?

If I ask these questions, it is not for the sake of wholesale condemnation of the old education. It is for quite another purpose. It is to emphasize the fact, first, that young people in traditional schools do have experiences; and, secondly, that the trouble is not the absence of experiences, but their defective and wrong character— wrong and defective from the standpoint of connection with further experience. The positive side of this point is even more important in connection with progressive education. It is not enough to insist upon the necessity of experience, nor even of activity in experience. Everything depends upon the *quality* of the experience which is had. The quality of any experience has two aspects. There is an immediate aspect of agreeableness or disagreeableness, and there is its influence upon later experiences. The first is obvious and easy to judge. The *effect* of an experience is not borne on its face. It sets a problem to the educator. It is his business to arrange for the kind of experiences which, while they do not repel the student, but rather engage his activities are, nevertheless, more than immediately enjoyable since they promote having desirable future experiences. Just as no man lives or dies to himself, so no experience lives and dies to itself. Wholly independent of desire or intent, every experience lives on in further experiences. Hence the central problem of an education based upon experience is to select the kind of present experiences that live fruitfully and creatively in subsequent experiences.

Later, I shall discuss in more detail the principle of the continuity of experience or what may be called the experiential continuum. Here I wish simply to emphasize the importance of this principle for the philosophy of educative experience. A philosophy of education, like any theory, has to be stated in words, in symbols. But so far as it is more than verbal it is a plan for conducting education. Like any plan, it must be framed with reference to what is to be done and how it is to be done. The more definitely and sincerely it is held that education is a development within, by, and for experience, the more important it is that there shall be clear conceptions of what experience is. Unless experience is so conceived that the result is a plan for deciding upon subject-matter, upon methods of instruction and discipline, and upon material equipment and social organization of the school, it is wholly in the air. It is reduced to a form of words which may be emotionally stirring but for which any other set of words might equally well be substituted unless they indicate operations to be initiated and executed. Just because traditional education was a matter of routine in which the plans and programs were handed down from the past, it does not follow that progressive education is a matter of planless improvisation.

The traditional school could get along without any consistently developed philosophy of education. About all it required in that line was a set of abstract words like culture, discipline, our great cultural heritage, etc., actual guidance being derived not from them but from custom and established routines. Just because progressive schools cannot rely upon established traditions and institutional habits, they must either proceed more or less haphazardly or be directed by ideas which, when they are made articulate and coherent, form a philosophy of education. Revolt against the kind of organization characteristic of the traditional school constitutes a demand for a kind of organization based upon ideas. I think that only slight acquaintance with the history of education is needed to prove that educational reformers and innovators alone have felt the need for a philosophy of education. Those who adhered to the established system needed merely a few fine-sounding words to justify existing practices. The real work was done by habits which were so fixed as to be institutional. The lesson for progressive education is that it requires in an urgent degree, a degree more pressing than was incumbent upon former innovators, a philosophy of education based upon a philosophy of experience.

I remarked incidentally that the philosophy in question is, to paraphrase the saying of Lincoln about democracy, one of education of, by, and for experience. No one of these words, *of, by,* or *for,* names anything which is self-evident. Each of them is a challenge to discover and put into operation a principle of order and organization which follows from understanding what educative experience signifies.

It is, accordingly, a much more difficult task to work out the kinds of materials, of methods, and of social relationships that are appropriate to the new education than is the case with traditional education. I think many of the difficulties experienced in the conduct of progressive schools and many of the criticisms leveled against them arise from this source. The difficulties are aggravated and the criticisms are increased when it is supposed that the new education is somehow easier than the old. This belief is, I imagine, more or less current. Perhaps it illustrates

again the *Either-Or* philosophy, springing from the idea that about all which is required is *not* to do what is done in traditional schools.

I admit gladly that the new education is *simpler* in principle than the old. It is in harmony with principles of growth, while there is very much which is artificial in the old selection and arrangement of subjects and methods, and artificiality always leads to unnecessary complexity. But the easy and the simple are not identical. To discover what is really simple and to act upon the discovery is an exceedingly difficult task. After the artificial and complex is once institutionally established and ingrained in custom and routine, it is easier to walk in the paths that have been beaten than it is, after taking a new point of view, to work out what is practically involved in the new point of view. The old Ptolemaic astronomical system was more complicated with its cycles and epicycles than the Copernican system. But until organization of actual astronomical phenomena on the ground of the latter principle had been effected the easiest course was to follow the line of least resistance provided by the old intellectual habit. So we come back to the idea that a coherent *theory* of experience, affording positive direction to selection and organization of appropriate educational methods and materials, is required by the attempt to give new direction to the work of the schools. The process is a slow and arduous one. It is a matter of growth, and there are many obstacles which tend to obstruct growth and to deflect it into wrong lines.

I shall have something to say later about organization. All that is needed, perhaps, at this point is to say that we must escape from the tendency to think of organization in terms of the *kind* of organization, whether of content (or subject-matter), or of methods and social relations, that mark traditional education. I think that a good deal of the current opposition to the idea of organization is due to the fact that it is so hard to get away from the picture of the studies of the old school. The moment "organization" is mentioned imagination goes almost automatically to the kind of organization that is familiar, and in revolting against that we are led to shrink from the very idea of any organization. On the other hand, educational reactionaries, who are now gathering force, use the absence of adequate intellectual and moral organization in the newer type of school as proof not only of the need of organization, but to identify any and every kind of organization with that instituted before the rise of experimental science. Failure to develop a conception of organization upon the empirical and experimental basis gives reactionaries a too easy victory. But the fact that the empirical sciences now offer the best type of intellectual organization which can be found in any field shows that there is no reason why we, who call ourselves emipiricists, should be "pushovers" in the matter of order and organization.

Experience—The Means and Goal of Education

John Dewey

IN WHAT I HAVE SAID I have taken for granted the soundness of the principle that education in order to accomplish its ends both for the individual learner and for society must be based upon experience—which is always the actual life-experience of some individual. I have not argued for the acceptance of this principle nor attempted to justify it. Conservatives as well as radicals in education are profoundly discontented with the present educational situation taken as a whole. There is at least this much agreement among intelligent persons of both schools of educational thought. The educational system must move one way or another, either backward to the intellectual and moral standards of a pre-scientific age or forward to ever greater utilization of scientific method in the development of the possibilities of growing, expanding experience. I have but endeavored to point out some of the conditions which must be satisfactorily fulfilled if education takes the latter course.

For I am so confident of the potentialities of education when it is treated as intelligently directed development of the possibilities inherent in ordinary experience that I do not feel it necessary to criticize here the other route nor to advance arguments in favor of taking the route of experience. The only ground for anticipating failure in taking this path resides to my mind in the danger that experience and the experimental method will not be adequately conceived. There is no discipline in the world so severe as the discipline of experience subjected to the tests of intelligent development and direction. Hence the only ground I can see for even a temporary reaction against the standards, aims, and methods of the newer education is the failure of educators who professedly adopt them to be faithful to them in practice. As I have emphasized more than once, the road of the new education is not an easier one to follow than the old road but a more strenuous and difficult one. It will remain so until it has attained its majority and that attainment will require many years of serious co-operative work on the part of its adherents. The greatest danger that attends its future is, I believe, the idea that it is an easy way to follow, so easy that its course may be improvised, if not in an impromptu fashion, at least almost from day to day or from week to week. It is for this reason that instead of extolling its principles, I have confined myself to showing certain conditions which must be fulfilled if it is to have the successful career which by right belongs to it.

I have used frequently in what precedes the words "progressive" and "new" education. I do not wish to close, however, without recording my firm belief that the fundamental issue is not of new versus old education nor of progressive against traditional education but a question of what anything whatever must be to be worthy of the name *education*. I am not, I hope and believe, in favor of any ends or any methods simply because the name progressive may be applied to them. The basic question concerns the nature of education with no qualifying adjectives prefixed. What we want and need is education pure and simple, and we shall make surer and faster progress when we devote ourselves to finding out just what education is and what conditions have to be satisfied in order that education may be a reality and not a name or a slogan. It is for this reason alone that I have emphasized the need for a sound philosophy of experience.

Gifts of Nature

Richard Louv

When I see birches bend to left and right . . .
I like to think some boy's been swinging them.
—ROBERT FROST

IF, WHEN WE WERE YOUNG, we tramped through forests of Nebraska cottonwoods, or raised pigeons on a rooftop in Queens, or fished for Ozark bluegills, or felt the swell of a wave that traveled a thousand miles before lifting our boat, then we were bound to the natural world and remain so today. Nature still informs our years—lifts us, carries us.

For children, nature comes in many forms. A newborn calf; a pet that lives and dies; a worn path through the woods; a fort nested in stinging nettles; a damp, mysterious edge of a vacant lot—whatever shape nature takes, it offers each child an older, larger world separate from parents. Unlike television, nature does not steal time; it amplifies it. Nature offers healing for a child living in a destructive family or neighborhood. It serves as a blank slate upon which a child draws and reinterprets the culture's fantasies. Nature inspires creativity in a child by demanding visualization and the full use of the senses. Given a chance, a child will bring the confusion of the world to the woods, wash it in the creek, turn it over to see what lives on the unseen side of that confusion. Nature can frighten a child, too, and this fright serves a purpose. In nature, a child finds freedom, fantasy, and privacy: a place distant from the adult world, a separate peace.

These are some of the utilitarian values of nature, but at a deeper level, nature gives itself to children—for its own sake, not as a reflection of a culture. At this level, inexplicable nature provokes humility.

As the preeminent nature poet Gary Snyder writes, we attach two meanings to the word "nature," which comes from the Latin *natura*—birth, constitution, character, course of things—and beyond *natura*, *nasci*—to be born. In its broadest interpretation, nature includes the material world and all of its objects and phenomena; by this definition, a machine is part of nature. So is toxic waste. The other meaning is what we call "the outdoors." By this connotation, a man-made thing is not a part of nature, but apart from nature. On its face, New York City may not appear natural, but it does contain all manner of hidden, self-organizing wild places, from the organisms secreted within the humus of Central Park to the hawks that circle above the Bronx. In this sense, a city complies with the broadest laws of nature; it is natural (as a machine is part of nature), but wild in its parts.

When considering children in nature, one hungers for a richer description, a definition with more breathing room—one that does not include *everything* as natural or restrict nature to virgin forest. Snyder is drawn to poet John Milton's phrase, "a wilderness of sweets." "Milton's usage of wilderness catches the very real condition of energy and richness that is so often found in wild systems. A 'wilderness of sweets' is like the billions of herring or mackerel babies in the ocean, the cubic miles of krill, wild prairie grass seed . . . all the incredible fecundity of small animals and plants, feeding the web," he explains. "But from another side, wilderness has implied chaos, eros, the unknown, realms of taboo, the habitat of both the ecstatic and the demonic. In both senses it is a place of archetypal power, teaching, and challenge." When we think of children and the gifts of nature, this third, more bountiful understanding is helpful. For the purpose of this book, when I use the word "nature" in a general way I mean natural wildness: biodiversity, abundance—related loose parts in a backyard or a rugged mountain ridge. Most of all, nature is reflected in our capacity for wonder. *Nasci.* To be born.

Though we often see ourselves as separate from nature, humans are also part of that wildness. My earliest memory of using my senses, and sensing wonder, came on a cold spring morning in Independence, Missouri. I was perhaps three years old, sitting in a dry field behind my grandmother's peeling Victorian home. Nearby, my father worked, planting a garden. He threw down a cigarette—as many were likely to do in that age, when Midwesterners habitually tossed refuse on the ground, or launched beer bottles and soda cans and cigarette butts from their car windows, sparks flying in the wind. The dry grass caught fire. I remember the exact sound of the flames and smell of the smoke and the *whoosh* of my father's leg and foot as he stamped and stepped quickly to chase the fire as it skipped across the field.

In this same field, I would walk around the fallen fruit from a pear tree, hold my nose and bend at the waist, a careful distance from the small mounds of ferment, and then experimentally inhale. I would sit down among the decaying fruit, attracted and repulsed. Fire and fermentation . . .

I spent hours exploring the woods and farmland at the suburban edge. There were the Osage orange trees, with thorny, unfriendly limbs that dropped sticky, foul fruit larger than softballs. Those were to be avoided. But within the windbreaks were trees that we could shinny, the small branches like the rungs of a ladder. We climbed fifty, sixty feet off the ground, far above the Osage windbreak, and from that vantage looked out upon the old blue ridges of Missouri, and the roofs of new houses in the ever-encroaching suburbs.

Often I climbed alone. Sometimes, lost in wonderment, I'd go deep into the woods, and imagine myself as Rudyard Kipling's Mowgli, the boy raised by wolves, and strip off most of my clothes for the ascent. If I climbed high enough, the branches thinned to the point where, when the wind came, the world would tip down and up and around and up

and to the side and up. It was frightening and wonderful to surrender to the wind's power. My senses were filled with the sensations of falling, rising, swinging; all around me the leaves snapped like fingers and the wind came in sighs and gruff whispers. The wind carried smells, too, and the tree itself surely released its scents faster in the gusts. Finally, there was only the wind that moved through everything.

Now, my tree-climbing days long behind me, I often think about the lasting value of those early, deliciously idle days. I have come to appreciate the long view afforded by those treetops. The woods were my Ritalin. Nature calmed me, focused me, and yet excited my senses.

"Where All the Electrical Outlets Are"

Many members of my generation grew into adulthood taking nature's gifts for granted; we assumed (when we thought of it at all) that generations to come would also receive these gifts. But something has changed. Now we see the emergence of what I have come to call nature-deficit disorder. This term is by no means a medical diagnosis, but it does offer a way to think about the problem and the possibilities—for children, and for the rest of us as well.

My own awareness of the transformation began in the late 1980s, during research for *Childhood's Future*, a book about the new realities of family life. I interviewed nearly three thousand children and parents across the country, in urban, suburban, and rural areas. In classrooms and living rooms, the topic of the children's relationship with nature sometimes surfaced. I think often of a wonderfully honest comment made by Paul, a fourth-grader in San Diego: "I like to play indoors better, 'cause that's where all the electrical outlets are."

In many classrooms I heard variations on that statement. True, for many children, nature still offers wonder. But for many others, playing in nature seemed so . . . Unproductive. Off-limits. Alien. Cute. Dangerous. Televised.

"It's all this *watching*," said a mother in Swarthmore, Pennsylvania.

"We've become a more sedentary society. When I was a kid growing up in Detroit, we were always outdoors. The kids who stayed indoors were the odd ones. We didn't have any huge wide-open spaces, but we were always outdoors on the streets—in the vacant lots, jumping rope, or playing baseball or hopscotch. We were out there playing even after we got older."

Another Swarthmore parent added, "Something else was different when we were young: our *parents* were outdoors. I'm not saying they were joining health clubs and things of that sort, but they were out of the house, out on the porch, talking to neighbors. As far as physical fitness goes, today's kids are the sorriest generation in the history of the United States. Their parents may be out jogging, but the kids just aren't outside."

This was the mantra among parents, grandparents, uncles, aunts, teachers, and other adults across the country, even in places I would have expected to have a different view. For example, I visited a middle-class neighborhood in suburban Overland Park, Kansas, not far from where I spent my teen years. In the intervening decades, many of the woods and fields had vanished, but enough natural landscape remained to at least provide the opportunity for outside play. Surely kids still played in nature here? Not often, said several parents, who came together in a living room one evening to talk about the new landscape of childhood. Though several lived on the same block, this was the first time that some of these parents had met each other.

"When our kids were in third or fourth grade, we still had a little field behind our place," said one mother. "The kids were complaining about being bored. And I said, 'Okay, you guys are bored? I want you to go out to that field, right there, and spend two hours. Find something to do there. Trust me; just try it one time. You might enjoy yourselves.' So, begrudgingly, they went out to the field. And they didn't come back in two hours—they came back much later. I asked them why, and they said, 'It was so much fun! We never dreamed we could have so much

fun!' They climbed trees; they watched things; they chased each other; they played games like we used to do when we were young. So the next day, I said, 'Hey, you guys are bored—why not go out to the field again?' And they answered, 'Nah—we've already done that once.' They weren't willing to let themselves do it again."

"I'm not sure I understand exactly what you're saying," responded a father. "I think that my girls enjoy things like a full moon, or a pretty sunset, or flowers. They enjoy the trees when they turn—that sort of thing."

Another mother in the group shook her head. "Sure, the little things, they notice," she said. "But they're distracted." She described the last time her family had gone skiing, in Colorado. "It was a perfect, quiet day, the kids are skiing down the mountain—and they've got their *headphones* on. They can't enjoy just hearing nature and being out there alone. They can't make their own entertainment. They have to bring something with them."

A quiet father, who had been raised in a farming community, spoke up.

"Where I grew up, a person was just *naturally* outdoors all the time," he said. "No matter which direction you went, you were outdoors— you were in a plowed field, or woods, or streams. We're not like that here. Overland Park is a metropolitan area now. Kids haven't lost anything, because they never had it in the first place. What we're talking about here is a transition made by most of us who grew up surrounded by nature. Now, nature's just not *there* anymore."

The group fell quiet. Yes, much of that once-wild land was being graded and built upon—but I could see woods from the windows of the house in which we were sitting. Nature *was* still out there. There was less of it, to be sure, but it was there just the same.

A day after talking with the Overland Park parents, I drove across the Kansas-Missouri border to Southwood Elementary School in Raytown, Missouri, near Kansas City. I attended grade school at Southwood. To my surprise, the same swings (or so it seemed) still creaked above the hot asphalt; the hallways still shone with the same linoleum tile; the same pint-sized wooden chairs, carved and initialed with black, blue, and red ink, sat waiting in crooked rows.

As the teachers gathered second- through fifth-graders and escorted them into the classroom where I waited, I unpacked my tape recorder and glanced out the window at the blue-green ridge of trees, probably pin oak, maple, cottonwood, or perhaps pecan or honey locust, their limbs shivering and swaying slowly in the spring breeze. How often, as a child, had those very trees inspired my daydreams?

During the next hour, as I asked the young people about their relationship with the outdoors, they described some of the barriers to going outside—lack of time, TV, the usual suspects. But the reality of these barriers did not mean that the children lacked curiosity. In fact, these kids spoke of nature with a strange mixture of puzzlement, detachment, and yearning—and occasional defiance. In the years to come, I would hear this tone often.

"My parents don't feel real safe if I'm going too deep in the woods," said one boy. "I just can't go too far. My parents are always worrying about me. So I'll just go, and usually not tell 'em where I'm going—so that makes 'em mad. But I'll just sit behind a tree or something, or lie in the field with all the rabbits."

One boy said computers were more important than nature, because computers are where the jobs are. Several said they were too busy to go outside. But one girl, a fifth-grader wearing a plain print dress and an intensely serious expression, told me she wanted to be a poet when she grew up.

"When I'm in the woods," she said, "I feel like I'm in my mother's shoes."

She was one of those exceptional children who do still spend time outside, in solitude. In her case nature represented beauty—and refuge. "It's so peaceful out there and the air smells so good. I mean, it's polluted, but not as much as the city air. For me, it's completely different there," she said. "It's like you're free when you go out there. It's your

own time. Sometimes I go there when I'm mad—and then, just with the peacefulness, I'm better. I can come back home happy, and my mom doesn't even know why."

Then she described her special part of the woods.

"I had a place. There was a big waterfall and a creek on one side of it. I'd dug a big hole there, and sometimes I'd take a tent back there, or a blanket, and just lie down in the hole, and look up at the trees and sky. Sometimes I'd fall asleep back in there. I just felt free; it was like my place, and I could do what I wanted, with nobody to stop me. I used to go down there almost every day."

The young poet's face flushed. Her voice thickened.

"And then they just cut the woods down. It was like they cut down part of me."

Over time I came to understand some of the complexity represented by the boy who preferred electrical outlets and the poet who had lost her special spot in the woods. I also learned this: Parents, educators, other adults, institutions—the culture itself—may say one thing to children about nature's gifts, but so many of our actions and messages—especially the ones we cannot hear ourselves deliver—are different.

And children hear very well.

The Third Frontier

Richard Louv

The frontier is a goner. It died with its boots laced.
—M. R. Montgomery

On my bookshelf is a copy of *Shelters, Shacks and Shanties,* written in 1915 by Daniel C. Beard, a civil engineer turned artist, best known as one of the founders of the Boy Scouts of America. For half a century, he wrote and illustrated a string of books on the outdoors. *Shelters, Shacks and Shanties* happens to be one of my favorite books because, particularly with his pen-and-ink drawings, Beard epitomizes a time when a young person's experience of nature was inseparable from the romantic view of the American frontier.

If such books were newly published today, they would be considered quaint and politically incorrect, to say the least. Their target audience was boys. The genre seemed to suggest that no self-respecting boy could enjoy nature without axing as many trees as possible. But what really defines these books, and the age they represented, is the unquestioned belief that being in nature was about *doing* something, about direct experience—and about not being a spectator.

"The smallest boys can build some of the simple shelters and the older boys can build the more difficult ones," Beard wrote in the foreword of *Shelters, Shacks and Shanties.* "The reader may, if he likes, begin with the first [shanty] and graduate by building the log houses; in doing this he will be closely following the history of the human race, because ever since our arboreal ancestors with prehensile toes scampered among the branches of the pre-glacial forests and built nest-like shelters in the trees, men have made themselves shacks for a temporary refuge." He goes on to describe, through words and drawings, how a boy could build some forty types of shelters, including the Tree-top House, the Adirondack, the Wick-Up, the Bark Teepee, the Pioneer, and the Scout. He tells "how to make beaver-mat huts" and "a sod house for the lawn." He teaches "how to split logs, make shakes, splits, or clapboards" and how to make a pole house, secret locks, an underground fort, and, intriguingly, "how to make a concealed log cabin inside of a modern house."

Today's reader would likely be impressed with the level of ingenuity and skill required, and the riskiness of some of the designs, too. In the case of the "original American boy's hogan or underground house," Beard does urge caution. During the creation of such caves, he admits, "there is always serious danger of the roof falling in and smothering the young troglodytes, but a properly built underground hogan is perfectly safe from such accidents."

I love Beard's books because of their charm, the era they conjure, and the lost art they describe. As a boy, I built rudimentary versions of these shelters, shacks, and shanties—including underground forts in the cornfields and elaborate tree houses with secret entrances and a view of what I imagined to be the frontier stretching from Ralston Street beyond the edge of the known suburban world.

Closing One Frontier, Opening Another

In the space of a century, the American experience of nature—culturally influential around the world—has gone from direct utilitarianism to romantic attachment to electronic detachment. Americans have passed not through one frontier, but through three. The third frontier—the one that young people are growing up in today—is every bit as much of a venture into the unknown as Daniel Beard experienced in his time.

The passing, and importance, of the first frontier was described in 1893, during Chicago's World's Columbian Exposition—a celebration of the 400th anniversary of Columbus's arrival in the Americas. There, at a meeting of the American Historical Association in Chicago, University of Wisconsin historian Frederick Jackson Turner presented his "frontier thesis." He argued that "the existence of an area of free land, its continuous recession, and the advance of American settlement westward" explained the development of the American nation, history, and character. He linked this pronouncement to results of the 1890 U.S. Census, which revealed the disappearance of a contiguous line of the American frontier—the "closing of the frontier." This was the same year that the superintendent of the census declared the end of the era of "free land"—that is, land available to homesteaders for tillage.

Little noted at the time, Jackson's thesis came to be considered one of the most important statements in American history. Jackson argued that every American generation had returned "to primitive conditions on a continually advancing frontier line." He described this frontier as "the meeting point between savagery and civilization." Basic American cultural traits could, he said, be linked to the influence of that frontier, including "that coarseness and strength combined with acuteness and acquisitiveness; that practical inventive turn of mind, quick to find expedients; that masterful grasp of material things . . . that restless, nervous energy; that dominant individualism." Historians still debate Turner's thesis; many, if not most, have rejected the frontier, as Turner saw it, as *the* key to understanding American history and sensibilities. Immigration, the industrial revolution, the Civil War—all had a deep formative influence on our culture. Turner himself later revised his theory to include events that were frontier-like—the oil boom of the 1890s, for example.

Nonetheless, from Teddy Roosevelt to Edward Abbey, Americans continued to think of themselves as frontier explorers. In 1905, at President Roosevelt's inauguration, cowboys rode down Pennsylvania Avenue,

the Seventh Cavalry passed for review, and American Indians joined the celebration—including the once-feared Geronimo. The parade, in fact, announced the coming of the second frontier, which existed mainly in the imagination for nearly a century. The second frontier existed in Beard's words and illustrations, and in the family farm, which, though already diminishing in number, continued as an important definer of American culture. Especially in the early decades of the twentieth century, the second frontier also existed in urban America; witness the creation of the great urban parks. The second frontier was a time, too, of suburban manifest destiny, when boys still imagined themselves woodsmen and scouts, and girls still yearned to live in a little house on the prairie—and sometimes built better forts than the boys.

If the first frontier was explored by the acquisitive Lewis and Clark, the second frontier was romanticized by Teddy Roosevelt. If the first frontier was the real Davy Crockett's, the second frontier peaked with Disney's Davy. If the first frontier was a time of struggle, the second frontier was a period of taking stock, of celebration. It brought a new politics of preservation, an immersion of Americans in the domesticated and romanticized fields and streams and woods around them.

Turner's 1893 pronouncement found its counterpart in 1993. His statement was based on the results of the 1890 Census; the new demarcation line was drawn from the 1990 Census. Eerily, one hundred years after Turner and the U.S. Census Bureau declared the end of what we usually consider the American frontier, the bureau posted a report that marked the death of the second frontier, and the birth of a third. That year, as the *Washington Post* reported, in "a symbol of massive national transformation," the federal government dropped its long-standing annual survey of farm residents. Farm population had dwindled so much—from 40 percent of U.S. households in 1900 to just 1.9 percent in 1990—that the farm resident survey was irrelevant. The 1993 report was surely as important as the census evidence that led to Turner's obituary for the frontier. "If sweeping changes can be captured in seemingly trivial benchmarks, the decision to end the annual report is one," reported the *Post*.

This new, symbolic demarcation line suggests that baby boomers—those born between 1946 and 1964—may constitute the last generation of Americans to share an intimate, familial attachment to the land and water. Many of us now in our forties or older knew farmland or forests at the suburban rim and had farm-family relatives. Even if we lived in an inner city, we likely had grandparents or other older relatives who farmed or had recently arrived from farm country during the rural-to-urban migration of the first half of the twentieth century. For today's young people, that familial and cultural linkage to farming is disappearing, marking the end of the second frontier.

The third frontier is populated by today's children.

Characteristics of the Third Frontier

In ways that neither Turner nor Beard could have imagined, the third frontier is shaping how the current generation, and many to come, will perceive nature.

Not yet fully formed or explored, this new frontier is characterized by at least five trends: a severance of the public and private mind from our food's origins; a disappearing line between machines, humans, and other animals; an increasingly intellectual understanding of our relationship with other animals; the invasion of our cities by wild animals (even as urban/suburban designers replace wildness with synthetic nature); and the rise of a new kind of suburban form. Most characteristics of the third frontier can be found in other technologically advanced countries, but these changes are particularly evident in the United States (if only because of the contrast with our frontier self-image). At first glance, these characteristics may not seem to fit together logically, but revolutionary times are seldom logical or linear.

In the third frontier, Beard's romantic images of the outdoor child seem as outdated as nineteenth-century depictions of the Knights of the Round Table. In the third frontier, heroes previously associated with the outdoors are irrelevant; the real Davy Crockett, who symbolized the first frontier, and even Disney's Davy, from the second frontier, are gone and nearly forgotten. A generation that came of age wearing buckskin jackets and granny dresses is now raising a generation for whom all fashion—piercing, tattoos, and all the rest—is urban.

- *For the young, food is from Venus; farming is from Mars*

My friend Nick Raven, who lives in Puerta de Luna, New Mexico, was a farmer for several years before he became a carpenter and then a teacher at a New Mexico prison. Nick and I have fished together for years, but we are very different men. I have described him as an undoubting nineteenth-century father; I am a doubting twenty-first-century dad. Nick believes fish should be caught and eaten; I believe that fish should be caught and, most of the time, released. Nick believes that violence is inevitable, that suffering is redemptive, and that a father must teach his children about the harshness of life by exposing them to that harshness. I believe that, as a parent, it's my job to protect my sons from the brutality of the world for as long as I can.

In an earlier book, *The Web of Life*, I described the relationship that Nick and his children had to animals and food:

> When Nick's children were small and he and his family still lived on their farm down a dirt road in a valley of adobes and cottonwoods and chiles, his daughter came home one day to find her favorite goat (not a pet, really, but one that followed her around) skinned, gutted, and strung up in the barn. This was a time when Nick's family was short on shoes, and the meat they ate was meat that Nick butchered or shot. It was a terrible moment for his daughter.
>
> Nick insists he has no regrets, but he still talks about it. She was hurt, he says, but she knew from that moment on, and will for the rest of her life, where the meat that she eats comes from, and that meat is not born plastic-wrapped. This is not the kind of experience I would have wanted for my children, but I have had a different life.

Few of us miss the more brutal aspects of raising food. For most young people, however, memory supplies no experience for comparison. More young people may be vegetarians or consume food from the health food store, but fewer are likely to raise their own food—especially if the food is an animal. In less than a half century, the culture has moved from a time when small family farms dominated the countryside—when Nick's way of understanding food was dominant—to a transitional time when many suburban families' vegetable gardens provided little more than recreation, to the current age of shrink-wrapped, lab-produced food. In one way, young people are more aware of the sources of what they eat. The animal-rights movement has taught them about the conditions within, say, poultry factory farms. It's probably no coincidence high school and college students are adopting vegetarianism in increasing numbers. Such knowledge, however, does not necessarily mean that the young are personally involved with their food sources.

• *The end of biological absolutes. Are we mice or are we men? Or both?*

The young are growing up in an era without biological absolutes. Even the definition of life itself is up for grabs.

One morning in 1997, people around the world opened their newspapers to see a disturbing photograph of a live, hairless mouse with what appeared to be a human ear growing from its back. The creature was the product of a team of researchers from the University of Massachusetts and the Massachusetts Institute of Technology that had introduced human cartilage cells into an earlike scaffold of biodegradable polyester fabric implanted onto the back of the mouse. The scaffold nourished the ersatz ear.

Since then, one headline after another has announced some potential blending of machines, humans, and other animals. The implications have evaded the public for two decades, according to the International Center for Technology Assessment, a nonprofit, bipartisan organization that assesses technological impacts on society. Human genes—including those for human growth and nerves—have been inserted into rats, mice, and primates to create creatures called chimera. These new creatures are to be used primarily for medical research, but some scientists seriously discuss the possibility of chimera someday existing outside the lab. In 2007, the chairman of the Department of Animal Biotechnology at the University of Nevada School of Medicine and his colleagues created the world's first human-sheep chimera, which has the body of a sheep and half-human organs. This line of research may lead to the common use of animal organs for human transplant surgeries.

Think what it means for children to grow up now, and how different their experience of nature and definition of life is, or soon will be, from the experiences of us adults. In our childhood, it was clear enough when a man was a man and a mouse was a mouse. Implicit in some of the newest technologies is the assumption that there's little difference between living and nonliving matter at the atomic and molecular level. Some see this as one more example of turning life into a commodity—the cultural reduction that turns living bodies into machines.

As the twenty-first century dawned, scientists at Cornell University reported building the first true nanomachine—near-microscopic robot—capable of movement; the minuscule robot used a propeller and motor and drew power from organic molecules. This development opened "the door to make machines that live inside the cell," one of the researchers said. "It allows us to merge engineered devices into living systems." At Sandia National Laboratories in Albuquerque, a scientist predicted that a system of "massively distributed intelligence" would vastly increase the nanorobots' ability to organize and communicate. "They will be able to do things collectively that they can't do individually, just like an ant colony," he said. Around the same time, an entomologist in Iowa created a machine combining moth antennae and microprocessors that sent signals of different pitches when the antennae picked up the scent of explosives. Researchers at Northwestern University created a miniature robot equipped with the brain stem of a lamprey eel. And a Rockville, Maryland, company engineered bacteria that could be functionally attached to microchips; the company called this invention "critters on a chip."

We can no longer assume a cultural core belief in the perfection of nature. To previous generations of children, few creations were as perfect or as beautiful as a tree. Now, researchers flood trees with genetic material taken from viruses and bacteria to make them grow faster, to create better wood products, or to enable trees to clean polluted soil. In 2003, the Pentagon's Defense Advanced Research Projects Agency funded researchers to develop a tree capable of changing colors when exposed to a biological or chemical attack. And the University of California promoted "birth control for trees," a genetically engineered method of creating a "eunuch-tree that spends more of its energy making wood and not love."

For baby boomers, such news is fascinating, strange, disturbing. To children growing up in the third frontier, such news is simply more hair on the dog—an assumed complexity.

• A hyperintellectualized perception of other animals

Not since the predominance of hunting and gathering have children been taught to see so many similarities between humans and other animals, though now those similarities are viewed in a very different, more intellectualized way.

This new understanding is based on science, rather than myth or religion. For example, recent studies reported in the journal *Science* describe how some nonhuman animals compose music. Analyses of songs of birds and humpback whales show they use some of the same acoustic techniques, and follow the same laws of composition, as those used by human musicians. Whale songs even contain rhyming refrains, and similar intervals, phrases, song durations, and tones. Whales also use rhyme in the way we do, "as a mnemonic device to help them remember complex material," the researchers write. According to their study,

whales physiologically have a choice: they could use arrhythmic and nonrepeating tunes, but instead, they sing.

Such information is not a substitute for direct contact with nature, but this kind of knowledge does inspire a certain wonder. My hope is that such research will cause children to be more inclined to cultivate a deeper understanding of their fellow creatures. Sure, romanticized closeness—say, swimming with dolphins at an animal touchy-feely resort—may soften some of our loneliness as a species. On the other hand, nature is not so soft and fuzzy. Fishing and hunting, for example, or the way Nick Raven put meat on his table, are messy—to some, morally messy—but removing all traces of that experience from childhood does neither children nor nature any good.

"You look at these kids [in the animal-rights movement], and you largely see urban, disaffected, but still privileged people," says Mike Two Horses, of Tucson, founder of the Coalition to End Racial Targeting of American Indian Nations. His organization supports native people such as the Northwest's Makah tribe, who are traditionally dependent on whale hunting. "The only animals the young animal rightists have ever known are their pets," he says. "The only ones they've ever seen otherwise are in zoos, Sea World, or on whale-watching [now whale-touching] expeditions. They've disconnected from the sources of their food—even from the sources of the soy and other vegetable proteins they consume."

I see more good in the animal-rights movement than Two Horses does, but his point has merit.

• Contact with nature: so close, and yet so far

Even as the definition of life itself is up for grabs, the potential for contact with more common wild animals is *increasing*, despite what Two Horses says. In a number of urban regions, humans and wild critters are coming into contact in ways that have been unfamiliar to Americans for at least a century. For one, the U.S. deer population is the highest it has been in a hundred years.

In *Ecology of Fear: Los Angeles and the Imagination of Disaster*, social historian and urban theorist Mike Davis describes what he calls a new dialectic between the "wild" and the "urban": "Metropolitan Los Angeles, now bordered primarily by mountains and desert rather than by farmland as in the past, has the longest wild edge, abruptly juxtaposing tract houses and wildlife habitat, of any major non-tropical city. . . . Brazen coyotes are now an integral part of the street scene in Hollywood and Toluca Lake." A reporter for the British newspaper the *Observer* writes: "[American] settlers and their descendants went about taming the environment with warlike ferocity. After ethnically cleansing the natives, they set about the extermination of bears, mountain lions, coyotes and wildfowl . . . but mountain lions adapted. Los Angeles may be the only city on earth with mountain lion victim support groups."

At midcentury, millions of Americans migrated to suburbia, following the dream of owning their own homes and a piece of land—their own quarter-acre of the frontier. For a while, space was expansive. Today, sprawl does not guarantee space. The newly dominant type of development—with interchangeable shopping malls, faux nature design, rigid control by community covenants and associations—dominates the bellwether metro regions of Southern California and Florida, but also encircles most of the older urban regions of the nation. These dense donuts of development offer fewer places for natural play than the earlier suburbs. In some cases, they offer even fewer natural play spaces than the centers of the old industrial cities.

In fact, parts of urban Western Europe are greener—in the sense of increasing the amount and quality of natural surroundings within urban regions—than most of urban/suburban America, a land still associated with frontier and open space. "An important lesson from many of these European cities has to do with the very perception we have of cities," writes Timothy Beatley, professor in the Department of Urban and Environmental Planning at the University of Virginia, in *Green Urbanism: Learning from European Cities*. Particularly in Scandinavian cities, where green design is gaining popularity, "there is a sense that cities are and ought to be places where nature occurs. In the United States, a challenge remains to overcome the polar distinction between what is *urban* and what is *natural*. Perhaps because of the expansiveness of our ecological resources and land base, we have tended to see the most significant forms of nature as occurring somewhere else—often hundreds of miles away from where most people actually live—in national parks, national seashores, and wilderness areas."

These are some of the trends that form the American context for a de-natured childhood, something that is perhaps as mysterious as—and certainly less studied than—the march of the nanorobots or the advance of the chimera.

Nature-Deficit Disorder and the Restorative Environment

Richard Louv

WITH IDEALISM AND TREPIDATION, a graduating college student anticipates becoming a teacher; but she is puzzled and upset by the school environment she experienced during her training. "With all of the testing in schools there is no time for physical education, let alone exploring the outdoors," she says. "In one of my kindergarten classes, the kids get to run to a fence and then run back. That's their P.E. They have to stay on the blacktop, or they can use one of the two swings available." She doesn't understand why P.E. is so limited, or why the playground can't be more conducive to natural play. Many educators share her sentiment.

At least her school has recess. In the United States, as the federal and state governments and local school boards have pushed for higher test scores in the first decade of the twenty-first century, nearly 40 percent of American elementary schools either eliminated or were considering eliminating recess. In the era of test-centric education reform and growing fear of liability, many districts considered recess a waste of potential academic time or too risky. "Lifers at Leavenworth get more time in the exercise yard," commented *Sports Illustrated* columnist Steve Rushin. School-based physical education was already on the wane. Between 1991 and 2003, the percentage of students who attended physical education class dropped from 42 percent to only 28 percent. Some states now allow students to earn P.E. credits *online*. Field trips were also cut. Even as school districts decreased students' experiences beyond the classroom walls, they increased the number of school hours. Ironically, the detachment of education from the physical world not only coincided with the dramatic rise in life-threatening childhood obesity but also with a growing body of evidence that links physical exercise and experience in nature to mental acuity and concentration.

Now, for some good news. Studies suggest that nature may be useful as a therapy for Attention Deficit Hyperactivity Disorder (ADHD), used with or, when appropriate, even replacing medications or behavioral therapies. Some researchers now recommend that parents and educators make available more nature experiences—especially green places—to children with ADHD, and thereby support their attentional functioning and minimize their symptoms. Indeed, this research inspires use of the broader term "nature-deficit disorder" as a way to help us better understand what many children experience, whether or not they have been diagnosed with ADHD. Again, I am not using the term nature-deficit disorder in a scientific or clinical sense. Certainly no academic researchers use the term, yet; nor do they attribute ADHD entirely to a nature deficit. But based on accumulating scientific evidence, I believe the concept—or hypothesis—of nature-deficit disorder is appropriate and useful as a layperson's description of one factor that may aggravate attentional difficulties for many children.

First, consider the diagnosis and current treatments of choice.

Nearly 8 million children in the U.S. suffer from mental disorders, and ADHD is one of the more prevalent ones. The disorder often develops before age seven, and is usually diagnosed between the ages of eight and ten. (Some people use the acronym ADD, for attention deficit disorder, to mean ADHD without the hyperactive component. But ADHD is the more accepted medical diagnosis.) Children with the syndrome are restless and have trouble paying attention, listening, following directions, and focusing on tasks. They may also be aggressive, even antisocial, and may suffer from academic failure. Or, in the language of the American Psychiatric Association: "The essential feature of ADHD is a persistent pattern of inattention and/or hyperactivity, impulsivity . . . more frequently displayed and more severe than is typically observed in individuals at a comparable level of development." Some of the uninformed public tends to believe that poor parenting and other social factors produce the immature behavior associated with ADHD, but ADHD is now considered by many researchers to be an organic disorder associated with differences in the brain morphology of children.

Critics charge that often-prescribed stimulant medications such as methylphenidate (Ritalin) and amphetamines (Dexedrine), though necessary in many cases, are overprescribed, perhaps as much as 10 to 40 percent of the time. Methylphenidate is a central nervous system stimulant and shares many of the pharmacological effects of amphetamine, methamphetamine, and cocaine. Contrasting sharply with medical practices elsewhere in the world, use of such stimulants in the United States increased 600 percent between 1990 and 1995, and continues to rise in numbers, especially for younger children. Between 2000 and 2003, spending on ADHD for preschoolers increased 369 percent. Both boys and girls are diagnosed with ADHD, but approximately 90 percent of the young people placed on medication—often at the suggestion of school officials—are boys.

One child psychiatrist explains: "My prejudice is that girls with ADHD whose symptoms are similar to boys with typical symptoms of ADHD are not common." Notice that he said "prejudice." Much about ADHD remains a medical and political mystery.

The massive increase in ADHD diagnoses and treatment may, in fact, be a matter of recognition: ADHD has been there all the time, called by other names or missed entirely, causing suffering for children and their families. Another explanation boils down to availability: three decades ago, the currently used medications were not widely known or as intensely marketed by pharmaceutical companies, and not yet fully

trusted by physicians—and we're lucky to have them now. Nonetheless, the use of such medications and the causes of ADHD are still in dispute. As of this writing, the latest culprit is television. The first study to link television-watching to this disorder was published in April 2004. Children's Hospital and Regional Medical Center in Seattle maintains that each hour of TV watched per day by preschoolers increases by 10 percent the likelihood that they will develop concentration problems and other symptoms of attention-deficit disorders by age seven.

This information is disturbing. But television is only part of the larger environmental/cultural change in our lifetime: namely, that rapid move from a rural to a highly urbanized culture. In an agricultural society, or during a time of exploration and settlement, or hunting and gathering—which is to say, most of mankind's history—energetic boys were particularly prized for their strength, speed, and agility. As mentioned earlier, as recently as the 1950s, most families still had some kind of agricultural connection. Many of these children, girls as well as boys, would have been directing their energy and physicality in constructive ways: doing farm chores, baling hay, splashing in the swimming hole, climbing trees, racing to the sandlot for a game of baseball. Their unregimented play would have been steeped in nature.

The "Restorative Environment"

Even without corroborating evidence or institutional help, many parents notice significant changes in their children's stress levels and hyperactivity when they spend time outside. "My son is still on Ritalin, but he's so much calmer in the outdoors that we're seriously considering moving to the mountains," one mother tells me. Could it simply be that he needs more physical activity? "No, he gets that, in sports," she says. Similarly, the back page of an October issue of *San Francisco* magazine displays a vivid photograph of a small boy, eyes wide with excitement and joy, leaping and running on a great expanse of California beach, storm clouds and towering waves behind him. A short article explains that the boy was hyperactive, he had been kicked out of his school, and his parents had not known what to do with him—but they had observed how nature engaged and soothed him. So for years they took their son to beaches, forests, dunes, and rivers to let nature do its work.

The photograph was taken in 1907. The boy was Ansel Adams. "Our brains are set up for an agrarian, nature-oriented existence that came into focus five thousand years ago," says Michael Gurian, a family therapist and best-selling author of *The Good Son* and *The Wonder of Boys*. "Neurologically, human beings haven't caught up with today's over-stimulating environment. The brain is strong and flexible, so 70 to 80 percent of kids adapt fairly well. But the rest don't. Getting kids out in nature can make a difference. We know this anecdotally, though we can't prove it yet."

New studies may offer that proof.

This research builds on the well-established attention-restoration theory, developed by a husband-and-wife research team, Stephen and Rachel Kaplan. Environmental psychologists at the University of Michigan, the Kaplans were inspired by philosopher and psychologist William James. In 1890, James described two kinds of attention: directed attention and fascination (i.e., involuntary attention). In the early 1970s, the Kaplans began a nine-year study for the U.S. Forest Service. They followed participants in an Outward Bound–like wilderness program, which took people into the wilds for up to two weeks. During these treks or afterward, subjects reported experiencing a sense of peace and an ability to think more clearly; they also reported that just being in nature was more restorative than the physically challenging activities, such as rock climbing, for which such programs are mainly known.

The positive effect of what the Kaplans came to call "the restorative environment" was vastly greater than the Kaplans expected it to be. According to the Kaplans' research, too much directed attention leads to what they call "directed-attention fatigue," marked by impulsive behavior, agitation, irritation, and inability to concentrate. Directed-attention fatigue occurs because neural inhibitory mechanisms become fatigued by blocking competing stimuli. As Stephen Kaplan explained in the journal *Monitor on Psychology*, "If you can find an environment where the attention is automatic, you allow directed attention to rest. And that means an environment that's strong on fascination." The fascination factor associated with nature is restorative, and it helps relieve people from directed-attention fatigue. Indeed, according to the Kaplans, nature can be the most effective source of such restorative relief.

In a paper presented to the American Psychological Society in 1993, the Kaplans surveyed more than twelve hundred corporate and state office workers. Those with a window view of trees, bushes, or large lawns experienced significantly less frustration and more work enthusiasm than those employees without such views. Like similar studies on stress reduction, this study demonstrated that a person does not have to live in the wilderness to reap nature's psychological benefits—including the ability to work better and think more clearly.

Subsequent research has supported the Kaplans' attention-restoration theory. For example, Terry A. Hartig, an associate professor of applied psychology at the Institute for Housing and Urban Research at Uppsala University in Gävle, Sweden, along with other researchers, compared three groups of backpacking enthusiasts; a group who went on a wilderness backpacking trip showed improved proofreading performance, while those who went on an urban vacation or took no vacation showed no improvement. In 2001, Hartig demonstrated that nature can help people recover from "normal psychological wear and tear"—but nature also improves the capacity to pay attention. Hartig emphasizes that he does not test the extremes—say, the Sierras versus East Los Angeles. Rather, his studies have focused on what he describes as "typical local conditions." As described in *Monitor on Psychology*, Hartig asked participants to complete a forty-minute sequence of tasks designed to exhaust their directed-attention capacity. After the attention-fatiguing tasks, Hartig then randomly assigned participants to spend forty minutes "walking in a local nature preserve, walking in an urban area, or sitting quietly while reading magazines and listening to music," the journal reported. "After this period, those who had walked in the nature preserve performed better than the other participants on a standard proofreading task. They also reported more positive emotions and less anger."

Nature's Ritalin

Attention-restoration theory applies to everyone, regardless of age. But what about children, especially those with ADHD?

"By bolstering children's attention resources, green spaces may enable children to think more clearly and cope more effectively with life stress," writes Nancy Wells, assistant professor at the New York State College of Human Ecology. In 2000, Wells conducted a study that found that being close to nature, in general, helps boost a child's attention span. When children's cognitive functioning was compared before and after they moved from poor- to better-quality housing adjacent to natural, green spaces, "profound differences emerged in their attention capacities even when the effects of the improved housing were taken into account," according to Wells.

Swedish researchers compared children within two day-care settings: at one, the quiet play area was surrounded by tall buildings, with low plants and a brick path; at the other, the play area, based on an "outdoors in all weather" theme, was set in an orchard surrounded by pasture and woods and was adjacent to an overgrown garden with tall trees and rocks. The study revealed that children in the "green" day care, who played outside every day, regardless of weather, had better motor coordination and more ability to concentrate.

Some of the most important work in this area has been done at the Human-Environment Research Laboratory at the University of Illinois. Andrea Faber Taylor, Frances Kuo, and William C. Sullivan have found that green outdoor spaces foster creative play, improve children's access to positive adult interaction—and relieve the symptoms of attention-deficit disorders. The greener the setting, the more the relief. By comparison, activities indoors, such as watching TV, or outdoors in paved, non-green areas, increase these children's symptoms.

In a survey of the families of ADHD children ages seven to twelve, parents or guardians were asked to identify after-school or weekend activities that left their child functioning especially well or particularly poorly. Activities were coded as "green" or "not green." Green activities, for example, included camping and fishing. Not-green activities included watching television, playing video games, doing homework. Some activities, such as rollerblading, were labeled ambiguous. The controls in this study were more complex than space allows me to describe, but suffice it to say, the research team was careful to account for variables. They found that greenery in a child's everyday environment, even views of green through a window, specifically reduces attention-deficit symptoms. While outdoor activities in general help, settings with trees and grass are the most beneficial. As they reported in the journal *Environment and Behavior,* "compared to the aftereffects of play in paved outdoor or indoor areas, activities in natural, green settings were far more likely to leave ADD children better able to focus, concentrate. Activities that left ADD children in worse shape were far more likely to occur indoors or outdoors in spaces devoid of greenery."

They also found that the positive influence of near-home nature on concentration may be more pronounced for girls (ages six to nine) than for boys. On average, the greener a girl's view from home, the better she concentrates, the less she acts impulsively, and the longer she can delay gratification. This helps her do better in school, handle peer pressure, and avoid dangerous, unhealthy, or problem behaviors. She is more likely to behave in ways that foster success in life, according to the researchers. Perhaps, if girls are less biologically prone to ADHD, as some mental health professionals believe, they may exhibit milder symptoms and may also have a more robust, healthy response to the treatment—whether pharmaceutical or green.

Based on the study, the University of Illinois issued this informal advice regarding girls to parents, caregivers, and others. The information also applies to boys:

- Encourage girls to study or play in rooms with a view of nature.
- Encourage children to play outdoors in green spaces, and advocate recess in green schoolyards. This may be especially helpful for renewing children's concentration.
- Plant and care for trees and vegetation at your residence, or encourage the owner to do so.
- Value and care for the trees in your community. Caring for trees means caring for people.

In addition to its work in the housing projects of inner-city Chicago, the Human-Environment Research Laboratory has also examined nature's impact on children with ADHD in middle-class settings. There, as in the public housing development, parents reported that their children exhibited fewer symptoms of ADHD after spending time in green surroundings. "You could say that the kids who had greener settings were just richer," says Kuo. "But that doesn't explain the fact that even rich kids do better after being in green settings. . . ." In the report:

> Participants were asked if they had had any experiences, either positive or negative, related to any aftereffects of green settings on their child's attention. One parent said she had recently begun taking her son to the local park for 30 minutes each morning before school because the weather was nice, and they "had some time to kill." She then said, "Come to think of it, I have noticed his attitude toward going to school has been better, and his schoolwork has been better this past week. I think it's because spending time at the park is pleasurable, peaceful, quiet, calming."

Another parent reported that his son could hit golf balls or fish for hours, and that during these times the boy was "very relaxed" and his attention-deficit symptoms minimal. "When I read the results of your study, they hit me in the face," he told the researchers. "I thought, yes, I've seen this!"

So had some of the parents I interviewed. Noticing that their children's ADHD symptoms were calmed by natural settings, they applied common sense; they were already encouraging their kids to spend more time outdoors, and they felt affirmed when I told them about the Illinois studies.

Taylor's and Kuo's more recent research findings are equally provocative. According to an unpublished study (which Taylor emphasizes is "a work in progress"), attention performance for unmedicated children clinically diagnosed with ADHD was better after a simple twenty-minute walk in a park, with a natural setting, than it was after a walk through well-kept downtown and residential areas.

Expanding such knowledge, and applying it in practical ways, will be the next challenge. Although today's common medications for ADHD offer temporary gains, including sustained attention and academic productivity, these medications may do little for a child's long-term success, either socially or academically. The medications can also have unpleasant side effects, among them sleep disruption, depression, and growth suppression of approximately half an inch per year on average, as reported in a large randomized trial funded by the National Institute of Mental Health. A second class of treatment—behavioral therapies—teaches children how to self-monitor attention and impulsive behavior, but the success of these therapies has been mixed.

More time in nature—combined with less television and more stimulating play and educational settings—may go a long way toward reducing attention deficits in children, and, just as important, increasing their joy in life. Researchers at the Human-Environment Research Laboratory believe that their findings point to nature therapy as a potential third course of treatment, applied either in concert with medication and/or behavioral therapy, or on its own. Behavioral therapy and nature therapy, if used collaboratively, might teach the young how to visualize positive experiences in nature when they need a calming tool. One psychiatrist who works with ADHD children relates how he sometimes slides into mild depressions. "I grew up fly-fishing in Michigan, and that was how I found peace as a child," he says. "So, when I begin to feel depressed, I use self-hypnosis to go there again, to call up those memories." He calls them "meadow memories." Though he is a firm believer in the proper use of the currently available medications for ADHD, he is encouraged by the possibility that nature therapy might offer him another professional tool. And, as Kuo points out, prescribing "green time" for the treatment of ADHD has other advantages: it's widely accessible, free of side effects, nonstigmatizing, and inexpensive.

If it's true that nature therapy reduces the symptoms of ADHD, then the converse may also be true: ADHD may be a set of symptoms aggravated by lack of exposure to nature. By this line of thinking, many children may benefit from medications, but the real disorder is less in the child than it is in the imposed, artificial environment. Viewed from this angle, the society that has disengaged the child from nature is most certainly disordered, if well-meaning. To take nature and natural play away from children may be tantamount to withholding oxygen.

An expanded application of attention-restoration theory would be useful in the design of homes, classrooms, and curricula. New York's Central Park, the first professionally designed urban park in America, was originally seen as a necessary aid to both civic consciousness and public health. It was construed as a place where all New Yorkers, regardless of class, age, or health, would benefit from fresh air. If nature-deficit disorder, as a hypothetical condition, affects all children (and adults) whether or not they have some biological propensity for attention deficit, then nature therapy at the societal and individual levels will do the greatest good for the greatest number of people.

Research on the impact of nature experiences on attention disorders and on wider aspects of child health and development is in its infancy, and easily challenged. Scientists doing some of the best of this research are the first to point that out. "For many of us, intuition emphatically asserts that nature is good for children," write Taylor and Kuo, in an overview of the research to date. "Beyond these intuitions, there are also well-reasoned theoretical arguments as to why humans in general—and therefore children—might have an inborn need for contact with nature." Yes, more research is needed, but we do not have to wait for it. As Taylor and Kuo argue, "Given the pattern of statistically reliable findings all pointing the same direction and persisting across different subpopulations of children, different settings, and in spite of design weaknesses, at some point it becomes more parsimonious to accept the fact that nature does promote healthy child development." If, as a growing body of evidence recommends, "contact with nature is as important to children as good nutrition and adequate sleep, then current trends in children's access to nature need to be addressed."

Even the most extensive research is unlikely to capture the full benefits of direct, natural experience. One aspect sure to elude measurement—a phenomenon that will be discussed later in these pages—is the contribution of nature to the spiritual life of the child, and therefore to the adult. This we know: As the sign over Albert Einstein's office at Princeton University read, "Not everything that counts can be counted, and not everything that can be counted counts." We don't have to wait for more, needed, research to act on common sense, or to give the gift of nature—even when it might seem to be too late.

Touching the Sky with a Stick

On a Sunday afternoon, a half-dozen teenagers gathered in defense attorney Daniel Ybarra's office not far from where I live. These teenagers—several diagnosed with ADHD—were on probation. They looked like your usual troubled teenage suspects: a gang member wearing a white net skullcap and black jersey; a girl with orange hair, her fingernails chewed to the quick; another boy with a black skullcap with a bandana tied around his head. He was wearing a sealskin Tlingit medicine pouch around his neck.

"You gonna carry your bus tokens in that, now?" one of the teens teased.

They had just returned from two chaperoned weeks living with tribal people in Ketchikan, Alaska, and in the southwestern Alaskan village of Kake, population 750. Kake is on an island served by a ferry that comes once every five days. The young people had been ordered to Alaska by a superior court judge who has an interest in alternative approaches to punishment.

For years, Ybarra had dreamed of pulling at-risk kids out of their urban environment and exposing them to nature. With the blessing of the judge, he acted. He persuaded Alaska Airlines to provide inexpensive airline tickets and raised contributions from law school classmates, a professional football player, and the United Domestic Workers union.

Some of the teenagers Ybarra took under his wing had never been to the mountains or beyond earshot of a combustion engine. The farthest one girl had been from her inner city home was a trip to a suburb. Suddenly they were transported to a place of glaciers and *takus*—storms that come out of nowhere, with winds that can blow a forest flat. They found themselves among grizzlies on the beaches, sea elephants that loomed up from the channel, and bald eagles that sat ten to a branch, as common as sparrows.

Tlingit villages face the sea, as they have for thousands of years, and life still revolves around the ocean's harvest. Although the Tlingits have their own problems with substance abuse, they retain pieces of what so many young people have lost. The boy with the black skullcap said: "I never seen a place so dark at night. I seen seals, bears, whales, salmon jumpin'—and I caught crabs and oysters, and as soon as we caught 'em,

we ate 'em. I felt like I was in a past life." A girl dressed in neo-hippie garb added: "I never saw a bear before. I'm scared of bears, but when I saw them, I had no stress. I was calm, free. You know what was great? Picking berries. It was addictive. Like cigarettes." She laughed. "Just the picking, just being out in the bushes."

One of the young men said he almost refused to get on the airplane to come home. But he returned determined to become an attorney specializing in environmental law.

They learned about *sha-a-ya-dee-da-na*, a Tlingit word that loosely translates as "self-respect," by being in nature, and by associating with people who had never been separated from it.

"I met a little boy and spent a lot of time with him," said one of the young women in the room. She had long, dark hair and eyes as bright as the midnight sun. "One day I was outside—this was right before we went into a sweat lodge—and he asked me, 'Can you touch the sky with a stick?' I answered, 'No, I'm too short.' He looked at me with disgust and said, 'You're weak! How do you know you can't touch the sky with a stick if you don't even try?'" Recalling the riddle, the young woman's eyes widened. "This was the first time I've ever been spoken to like that by a four-year-old."

When she came home, her mother was not at the airport to pick her up. She returned to an empty house.

"Last night, I looked out at the trees and I thought of Kake," she said.

Anyone who has spent much time around addicts or gang members understands how disarming—and manipulative—they can be. Yet on this afternoon, I saw no evidence of the con artist in their eyes. At least for a while—a day, a week, a year, or perhaps even a lifetime—they were changed.

The Land Ethic

Aldo Leopold

WHEN GOD-LIKE Odysseus returned from the wars in Troy, he hanged all on one rope a dozen slave-girls of his household whom he suspected of misbehavior during his absence.

This hanging involved no question of propriety. The girls were property. The disposal of property was then, as now, a matter of expediency, not of right and wrong.

Concepts of right and wrong were not lacking from Odysseus' Greece: witness the fidelity of his wife through the long years before at last his black-prowed galleys clove the wine-dark seas for home. The ethical structure of that day covered wives, but had not yet been extended to human chattels. During the three thousand years which have since elapsed, ethical criteria have been extended to many fields of conduct, with corresponding shrinkages in those judged by expediency only.

This extension of ethics, so far studied only by philosophers, is actually a process in ecological evolution. Its sequences may be described in ecological as well as in philosophical terms. An ethic, ecologically, is a limitation on freedom of action in the struggle for existence. An ethic, philosophically, is a differentiation of social from anti-social conduct. These are two definitions of one thing. The thing has its origin in the tendency of interdependent individuals or groups to evolve modes of co-operation. The ecologist calls these symbioses. Politics and economics are advanced symbioses in which the original free-for-all competition has been replaced, in part, by co-operative mechanisms with an ethical content.

The complexity of co-operative mechanisms has increased with population density, and with the efficiency of tools. It was simpler, for example, to define the anti-social uses of sticks and stones in the days of the mastodons than of bullets and billboards in the age of motors.

The first ethics dealt with the relation between individuals; the Mosaic Decalogue is an example. Later accretions dealt with the relation between the individual and society. The Golden Rule tries to integrate the individual to society; democracy to integrate social organization to the individual.

There is as yet no ethic dealing with man's relation to land and to the animals and plants which grow upon it. Land, like Odysseus' slave-girls, is still property. The land-relation is still strictly economic, entailing privileges but not obligations.

The extension of ethics to this third element in human environment is, if I read the evidence correctly, an evolutionary possibility and an ecological necessity. It is the third step in a sequence. The first two have already been taken. Individual thinkers since the days of Ezekiel and Isaiah have asserted that the despoliation of land is not only inexpedient but wrong. Society, however, has not yet affirmed their belief. I regard the present conservation movement as the embryo of such an affirmation.

An ethic may be regarded as a mode of guidance for meeting ecological situations so new or intricate, or involving such deferred reactions, that the path of social expediency is not discernible to the average individual. Animal instincts are modes of guidance for the individual in meeting such situations. Ethics are possibly a kind of community instinct in-the-making.

The Community Concept

All ethics so far evolved rest upon a single premise: that the individual is a member of a community of interdependent parts. His instincts prompt him to compete for his place in the community, but his ethics prompt him also to co-operate (perhaps in order that there may be a place to compete for).

The land ethic simply enlarges the boundaries of the community to include soils, waters, plants, and animals, or collectively: the land.

This sounds simple: do we not already sing our love for and obligation to the land of the free and the home of the brave? Yes, but just what and whom do we love? Certainly not the soil, which we are sending helter-skelter downriver. Certainly not the waters, which we assume have no function except to turn turbines, float barges, and carry off sewage. Certainly not the plants, of which we exterminate whole communities without batting an eye. Certainly not the animals, of which we have already extirpated many of the largest and most beautiful species. A land ethic of course cannot prevent the alteration, management, and use of these 'resources,' but it does affirm their right to continued existence, and, at least in spots, their continued existence in a natural state.

In short, a land ethic changes the role of *Homo sapiens* from conqueror of the land-community to plain member and citizen of it. It implies respect for his fellow-members, and also respect for the community as such.

In human history, we have learned (I hope) that the conqueror role is eventually self-defeating. Why? Because it is implicit in such a role that the conqueror knows, *ex cathedra*, just what makes the community clock tick, and just what and who is valuable, and what and who is worthless, in community life. It always turns out that he knows neither, and this is why his conquests eventually defeat themselves.

In the biotic community, a parallel situation exists. Abraham knew exactly what the land was for: it was to drip milk and honey into Abraham's mouth. At the present moment, the assurance with which we regard this assumption is inverse to the degree of our education.

The ordinary citizen today assumes that science

29

knows what makes the community clock tick; the scientist is equally sure that he does not. He knows that the biotic mechanism is so complex that its workings may never be fully understood.

That man is, in fact, only a member of a biotic team is shown by an ecological interpretation of history. Many historical events, hitherto explained solely in terms of human enterprise, were actually biotic interactions between people and land. The characteristics of the land determined the facts quite as potently as the characteristics of the men who lived on it.

Consider, for example, the settlement of the Mississippi valley. In the years following the Revolution, three groups were contending for its control: the native Indian, the French and English traders, and the American settlers. Historians wonder what would have happened if the English at Detroit had thrown a little more weight into the Indian side of those tipsy scales which decided the outcome of the colonial migration into the cane-lands of Kentucky. It is time now to ponder the fact that the cane-lands, when subjected to the particular mixture of forces represented by the cow, plow, fire, and axe of the pioneer, became bluegrass. What if the plant succession inherent in this dark and bloody ground had, under the impact of these forces, given us some worthless sedge, shrub, or weed? Would Boone and Kenton have held out? Would there have been any overflow into Ohio, Indiana, Illinois, and Missouri? Any Louisiana Purchase? Any transcontinental union of new states? Any Civil War?

Kentucky was one sentence in the drama of history.

We are commonly told what the human actors in this drama tried to do, but we are seldom told that their success, or the lack of it, hung in large degree on the reaction of particular soils to the impact of the particular forces exerted by their occupancy. In the case of Kentucky, we do not even know where the bluegrass came from—whether it is a native species, or a stowaway from Europe.

Contrast the cane-lands with what hindsight tells us about the Southwest, where the pioneers were equally brave, resourceful, and persevering. The impact of occupancy here brought no bluegrass, or other plant fitted to withstand the bumps and buffetings of hard use. This region, when grazed by livestock, reverted through a series of more and more worthless grasses, shrubs, and weeds to a condition of unstable equilibrium. Each recession of plant types bred erosion; each increment to erosion bred a further recession of plants. The result today is a progressive and mutual deterioration, not only of plants and soils, but of the animal community subsisting thereon. The early settlers did not expect this: on the ciénegas of New Mexico some even cut ditches to hasten it. So subtle has been its progress that few residents of the region are aware of it. It is quite invisible to the tourist who finds this wrecked landscape colorful and charming (as indeed it is, but it bears scant resemblance to what it was in 1848).

This same landscape was 'developed' once before, but with quite different results. The Pueblo Indians settled the Southwest in pre-Columbian times, but they happened *not* to be equipped with range livestock. Their civilization expired, but not because their land expired.

In India, regions devoid of any sod-forming grass have been settled, apparently without wrecking the land, by the simple expedient of carrying the grass to the cow, rather than vice versa. (Was this the result of some deep wisdom, or was it just good luck? I do not know.)

In short, the plant succession steered the course of history; the pioneer simply demonstrated, for good or ill, what successions inhered in the land. Is history taught in this spirit? It will be, once the concept of land as a community really penetrates our intellectual life.

The Ecological Conscience

Conservation is a state of harmony between men and land. Despite nearly a century of propaganda, conservation still proceeds at a snail's pace; progress still consists largely of letterhead pieties and convention oratory. On the back forty we still slip two steps backward for each forward stride.

The usual answer to this dilemma is 'more conservation education.' No one will debate this, but is it certain that only the *volume* of education needs stepping up? Is something lacking in the *content* as well?

It is difficult to give a fair summary of its content in brief form, but, as I understand it, the content is substantially this: obey the law, vote right, join some organizations, and practice what conservation is prof-

itable on your own land; the government will do the rest.

Is not this formula too easy to accomplish anything worth-while? It defines no right or wrong, assigns no obligation, calls for no sacrifice, implies no change in the current philosophy of values. In respect of land-use, it urges only enlightened self-interest. Just how far will such education take us? An example will perhaps yield a partial answer.

By 1930 it had become clear to all except the ecologically blind that southwestern Wisconsin's topsoil was slipping seaward. In 1933 the farmers were told that if they would adopt certain remedial practices for five years, the public would donate CCC labor to install them, plus the necessary machinery and materials. The offer was widely accepted, but the practices were widely forgotten when the five-year contract period was up. The farmers continued only those practices that yielded an immediate and visible economic gain for themselves.

This led to the idea that maybe farmers would learn more quickly if they themselves wrote the rules. Accordingly the Wisconsin Legislature in 1937 passed the Soil Conservation District Law. This said to farmers, in effect: *We, the public, will furnish you free technical service and loan you specialized machinery, if you will write your own rules for land-use. Each county may write its own rules, and these will have the force of* law. Nearly all the counties promptly organized to accept the proffered help, but after a decade of operation, *no county has yet written a single rule.* There has been visible progress in such practices as strip-cropping, pasture renovation, and soil liming, but none in fencing woodlots against grazing, and none in excluding plow and cow from steep slopes. The farmers, in short, have selected those remedial practices which were profitable anyhow, and ignored those which were profitable to the community, but not clearly profitable to themselves.

When one asks why no rules have been written, one is told that the community is not yet ready to support them; education must precede rules. But the education actually in progress makes no mention of obligations to land over and above those dictated by self-interest. The net result is that we have more education but less soil, fewer healthy woods, and as many floods as in 1937.

The puzzling aspect of such situations is that the existence of obligations over and above self-interest is taken for granted in such rural community enterprises as the betterment of roads, schools, churches, and baseball teams. Their existence is not taken for granted, nor as yet seriously discussed, in bettering the behavior of the water that falls on the land, or in the preserving of the beauty or diversity of the farm landscape. Land-use ethics are still governed wholly by economic self-interest, just as social ethics were a century ago.

To sum up: we asked the farmer to do what he conveniently could to save his soil, and he has done just that, and only that. The farmer who clears the woods off a 75 percent slope, turns his cows into the clearing, and dumps its rainfall, rocks, and soil into the community creek, is still (if otherwise decent) a respected member of society. If he puts lime on his fields and plants his crops on contour, he is still

entitled to all the privileges and emoluments of his Soil Conservation District. The District is a beautiful piece of social machinery, but it is coughing along on two cylinders because we have been too timid, and too anxious for quick success, to tell the farmer the true magnitude of his obligations. Obligations have no meaning without conscience, and the problem we face is the extension of the social conscience from people to land.

No important change in ethics was ever accomplished without an internal change in our intellectual emphasis, loyalties, affections, and convictions. The proof that conservation has not yet touched these foundations of conduct lies in the fact that philosophy and religion have not yet heard of it. In our attempt to make conservation easy, we have made it trivial.

Substitutes for a Land Ethic

When the logic of history hungers for bread and we hand out a stone, we are at pains to explain how much the stone resembles bread. I now describe some of the stones which serve in lieu of a land ethic.

One basic weakness in a conservation system based wholly on economic motives is that most members of the land community have no economic value. Wildflowers and songbirds are examples. Of the 22,000 higher plants and animals native to Wisconsin, it is doubtful whether more than 5 per cent can be sold, fed, eaten, or otherwise put to economic use. Yet these creatures are members of the biotic community, and if (as I believe) its stability depends on its integrity, they are entitled to continuance.

When one of these non-economic categories is threatened, and if we happen to love it, we invent subterfuges to give it economic importance. At the beginning of the century songbirds were supposed to be disappearing. Ornithologists jumped to the rescue with some distinctly shaky evidence to the effect that insects would eat us up if birds failed to control them. The evidence had to be economic in order to be valid.

It is painful to read these circumlocutions today. We have no land ethic yet, but we have at least drawn nearer the point of admitting that birds should continue as a matter of biotic right, regardless of the presence or absence of economic advantage to us.

A parallel situation exists in respect of predatory mammals, raptorial birds, and fish-eating birds. Time was when biologists somewhat overworked the evidence that these creatures preserve the health of game by killing weaklings, or that they control rodents for the farmer, or that they prey only on 'worthless' species. Here again, the evidence had to be economic in order to be valid. It is only in recent years that we hear the more honest argument that predators are members of the community, and that no special interest has the right to exterminate them for the sake of a benefit, real or fancied, to itself. Unfortunately this enlightened view is still in the talk stage. In the field the extermination of predators goes merrily on: witness the impending erasure of the timber wolf by fiat of Congress, the Conservation Bureaus, and many state legislatures.

Some species of trees have been 'read out of the party' by economics-minded foresters because they grow too slowly, or have too low a sale value to pay as timber crops: white cedar, tamarack, cypress, beech, and hemlock are examples. In Europe, where forestry is ecologically more advanced, the non-commercial tree species are recognized as members of the native forest community, to be preserved as such, within reason. Moreover some (like beech) have been found to have a valuable function in building up soil fertility. The interdependence of the forest and its constituent tree species, ground flora, and fauna is taken for granted.

Lack of economic value is sometimes a character not only of species or groups, but of entire biotic communities: marshes, bogs, dunes, and 'deserts' are examples. Our formula in such cases is to relegate their conservation to government as refuges, monuments, or parks. The difficulty is that these communities are usually interspersed with more valuable private lands; the government cannot possibly own or control such scattered parcels. The net effect is that we have relegated some of them to ultimate extinction over large areas. If the private owner were ecologically minded, he would be proud to be the custodian of a reasonable proportion of such areas, which add diversity and beauty to his farm and to his community.

In some instances, the assumed lack of profit in these 'waste' areas has proved to be wrong, but only after most of them had been done away with. The present scramble to reflood muskrat marshes is a case in point.

There is a clear tendency in American conservation

to relegate to government all necessary jobs that private landowners fail to perform. Government ownership, operation, subsidy, or regulation is now widely prevalent in forestry, range management, soil and watershed management, park and wilderness conservation, fisheries management, and migratory bird management, with more to come. Most of this growth in governmental conservation is proper and logical, some of it is inevitable. That I imply no disapproval of it is implicit in the fact that I have spent most of my life working for it. Nevertheless the question arises: What is the ultimate magnitude of the enterprise? Will the tax base carry its eventual ramifications? At what point will governmental conservation, like the mastodon, become handicapped by its own dimensions? The answer, if there is any, seems to be in a land ethic, or some other force which assigns more obligation to the private landowner.

Industrial landowners and users, especially lumbermen and stockmen, are inclined to wail long and loudly about the extension of government ownership and regulation to land, but (with notable exceptions) they show little disposition to develop the only visible alternative: the voluntary practice of conservation on their own lands.

When the private landowner is asked to perform some unprofitable act for the good of the community, he today assents only with outstretched palm. If the act costs him cash this is fair and proper, but when it costs only fore-thought, open-mindedness, or time, the issue is at least debatable. The overwhelming growth of land-use subsidies in recent years must be ascribed, in large part, to the government's own agencies for conservation education: the land bureaus, the agricultural colleges, and the extension services. As far as I can detect, no ethical obligation toward land is taught in these institutions.

To sum up: a system of conservation based solely on economic self-interest is hopelessly lopsided. It tends to ignore, and thus eventually to eliminate, many elements in the land community that lack commercial value, but that are (as far as we know) essential to its healthy functioning. It assumes, falsely, I think, that the economic parts of the biotic clock will function without the uneconomic parts. It tends to relegate to government many functions eventually too large, too complex, or too widely dispersed to be performed by government.

An ethical obligation on the part of the private owner is the only visible remedy for these situations.

The Land Pyramid

An ethic to supplement and guide the economic relation to land presupposes the existence of some mental image of land as a biotic mechanism. We can be ethical only in relation to something we can see, feel, understand, love, or otherwise have faith in.

The image commonly employed in conservation education is 'the balance of nature.' For reasons too lengthy to detail here, this figure of speech fails to describe accurately what little we know about the land mechanism. A much truer image is the one employed in ecology: the biotic pyramid. I shall first sketch the pyramid as a symbol of land, and later develop some of its implications in terms of land-use.

Plants absorb energy from the sun. This energy flows through a circuit called the biota, which may be represented by a pyramid consisting of layers. The bottom layer is the soil. A plant layer rests on the soil, an insect layer on the plants, a bird and rodent layer on the insects, and so on up through various animal groups to the apex layer, which consists of the larger carnivores.

The species of a layer are alike not in where they came from, or in what they look like, but rather in what they eat. Each successive layer depends on those below it for food and often for other services, and each in turn furnishes food and services to those above. Proceeding upward, each successive layer decreases in numerical abundance. Thus, for every carnivore there are hundreds of his prey, thousands of their prey, millions of insects, uncountable plants. The pyramidal form of the system reflects this numerical progression from apex to base. Man shares an intermediate layer with the bears, raccoons, and squirrels which eat both meat and vegetables.

The lines of dependency for food and other services are called food chains. Thus soil-oak-deer-Indian is a chain that has now been largely converted to soil-corn-cow-farmer. Each species, including ourselves, is a link in many chains. The deer eats a hundred plants other than oak, and the cow a hundred plants other than corn. Both, then, are links in a hundred chains. The pyramid is a tangle of chains so complex as to seem disorderly, yet the stability of the system proves it to be a highly organized structure. Its functioning depends on the co-operation and competition of its diverse parts.

In the beginning, the pyramid of life was low and squat; the food chains short and simple. Evolution has added layer after layer, link after link. Man is one of thousands of accretions to the height and complexity of the pyramid. Science has given us many doubts, but it has given us at least one certainty: the trend of evolution is to elaborate and diversify the biota.

Land, then, is not merely soil; it is a fountain of energy flowing through a circuit of soils, plants, and animals. Food chains are the living channels which conduct energy upward; death and decay return it to the soil. The circuit is not closed; some energy is dissipated in decay, some is added by absorption from the air, some is stored in soils, peats, and long-lived forests; but it is a sustained circuit, like a slowly augmented revolving fund of life. There is always a net loss by downhill wash, but this is normally small and offset by the decay of rocks. It is deposited in the ocean and, in the course of geological time, raised to form new lands and new pyramids.

The velocity and character of the upward flow of energy depend on the complex structure of the plant and animal community, much as the upward flow of sap in a tree depends on its complex cellular organization. Without this complexity, normal circulation would presumably not occur. Structure means the characteristic numbers, as well as the characteristic kinds and functions, of the component species. This interdependence between the complex structure of the land and its smooth functioning as an energy unit is one of its basic attributes.

When a change occurs in one part of the circuit, many other parts must adjust themselves to it. Change does not necessarily obstruct or divert the flow of energy; evolution is a long series of self-induced changes, the net result of which has been to elaborate the flow mechanism and to lengthen the circuit. Evolutionary changes, however, are usually slow and local. Man's invention of tools has enabled him to make changes of unprecedented violence, rapidity, and scope.

One change is in the composition of floras and faunas. The larger predators are lopped off the apex of the pyramid; food chains, for the first time in history, become shorter rather than longer. Domesticated species from other lands are substituted for wild ones, and wild ones are moved to new habitats. In this world-wide pooling of faunas and floras, some species get out of bounds as pests and diseases, others are extinguished. Such effects are seldom intended or foreseen; they represent unpredicted and often untraceable readjustments in the structure. Agricultural science is largely a race between the emergence of new pests and the emergence of new techniques for their control.

Another change touches the flow of energy through plants and animals and its return to the soil. Fertility is the ability of soil to receive, store, and release energy. Agriculture, by overdrafts on the soil, or by too radical a substitution of domestic for native species in the superstructure, may derange the channels of flow or deplete storage. Soils depleted of their storage,

or of the organic matter which anchors it, wash away faster than they form. This is erosion.

Waters, like soil, are part of the energy circuit. Industry, by polluting waters or obstructing them with dams, may exclude the plants and animals necessary to keep energy in circulation.

Transportation brings about another basic change: the plants or animals grown in one region are now consumed and returned to the soil in another. Transportation taps the energy stored in rocks, and in the air, and uses it elsewhere; thus we fertilize the garden with nitrogen gleaned by the guano birds from the fishes of seas on the other side of the Equator. Thus the formerly localized and self-contained circuits are pooled on a world-wide scale.

The process of altering the pyramid for human occupation releases stored energy, and this often gives rise, during the pioneering period, to a deceptive exuberance of plant and animal life, both wild and tame. These releases of biotic capital tend to becloud or postpone the penalties of violence.

*   *   *

This thumbnail sketch of land as an energy circuit conveys three basic ideas:

(1) That land is not merely soil.

(2) That the native plants and animals kept the energy circuit open; others may or may not.

(3) That man-made changes are of a different order than evolutionary changes, and have effects more comprehensive than is intended or foreseen.

These ideas, collectively, raise two basic issues: Can the land adjust itself to the new order? Can the desired alterations be accomplished with less violence?

Biotas seem to differ in their capacity to sustain violent conversion. Western Europe, for example, carries a far different pyramid than Caesar found there. Some large animals are lost; swampy forests have become meadows or plowland; many new plants and animals are introduced, some of which escape as pests; the remaining natives are greatly changed in distribution and abundance. Yet the soil is still there and, with the help of imported nutrients, still fertile; the waters flow normally; the new structure seems to function and to persist. There is no visible stoppage or derangement of the circuit.

Western Europe, then, has a resistant biota. Its inner processes are tough, elastic, resistant to strain. No matter how violent the alterations, the pyramid, so far, has developed some new *modus vivendi* which preserves its habitability for man, and for most of the other natives.

Japan seems to present another instance of radical conversion without disorganization.

Most other civilized regions, and some as yet barely touched by civilization, display various stages of disorganization, varying from initial symptoms to advanced wastage. In Asia Minor and North Africa diagnosis is confused by climatic changes, which may have been either the cause or the effect of advanced wastage. In the United States the degree of disorganization varies locally; it is worst in the Southwest, the Ozarks, and parts of the South, and least in New England and the Northwest. Better land-uses may still arrest it in the less advanced regions. In parts of

Mexico, South America, South Africa, and Australia a violent and accelerating wastage is in progress, but I cannot assess the prospects.

This almost world-wide display of disorganization in the land seems to be similar to disease in an animal, except that it never culminates in complete disorganization or death. The land recovers, but at some reduced level of complexity, and with a reduced carrying capacity for people, plants, and animals. Many biotas currently regarded as 'lands of opportunity' are in fact already subsisting on exploitative agriculture, i.e. they have already exceeded their sustained carrying capacity. Most of South America is overpopulated in this sense.

In arid regions we attempt to offset the process of wastage by reclamation, but it is only too evident that the prospective longevity of reclamation projects is often short. In our own West, the best of them may not last a century.

The combined evidence of history and ecology seems to support one general deduction: the less violent the man-made changes, the greater the probability of successful readjustment in the pyramid. Violence, in turn, varies with human population density; a dense population requires a more violent conversion. In this respect, North America has a better chance for permanence than Europe, if she can contrive to limit her density.

This deduction runs counter to our current philosophy, which assumes that because a small increase in density enriched human life, that an indefinite increase will enrich it indefinitely. Ecology knows of no density relationship that holds for indefinitely wide limits. All gains from density are subject to a law of diminishing returns.

Whatever may be the equation for men and land, it is improbable that we as yet know all its terms. Recent discoveries in mineral and vitamin nutrition reveal unsuspected dependencies in the up-circuit: incredibly minute quantities of certain substances determine the value of soils to plants, of plants to animals. What of the down-circuit? What of the vanishing species, the preservation of which we now regard as an esthetic luxury? They helped build the soil; in what unsuspected ways may they be essential to its maintenance? Professor Weaver proposes that we use prairie flowers to reflocculate the wasting soils of the dust bowl; who knows for what purpose cranes and condors, otters and grizzlies may some day be used?

Land Health and the A-B Cleavage

A land, ethic, then, reflects the existence of an ecological conscience, and this in turn reflects a conviction of individual responsibility for the health of the land. Health is the capacity of the land for self-renewal. Conservation is our effort to understand and preserve this capacity.

Conservationists are notorious for their dissensions. Superficially these seem to add up to mere confusion, but a more careful scrutiny reveals a single plane of cleavage common to many specialized fields. In each field one group (A) regards the land as soil, and its function as commodity-production; another group (B) regards the land as a biota, and its function as something broader. How much broader is admittedly in a state of doubt and confusion.

In my own field, forestry, group A is quite content to grow trees like cabbages, with cellulose as the basic forest commodity. It feels no inhibition against violence; its ideology is agronomic. Group B, on the other hand, sees forestry as fundamentally different from agronomy because it employs natural species, and manages a natural environment rather than creating an artificial one. Group B prefers natural reproduction on principle. It worries on biotic as well as economic grounds about the loss of species like chestnut, and the threatened loss of the white pines. It worries about a whole series of secondary forest functions: wildlife, recreation, watersheds, wilderness areas. To my mind, Group B feels the stirrings of an ecological conscience.

In the wildlife field, a parallel cleavage exists. For Group A the basic commodities are sport and meat; the yardsticks of production are ciphers of take in pheasants and trout. Artificial propagation is acceptable as a permanent as well as a temporary recourse—if its unit costs permit. Group B, on the other hand, worries about a whole series of biotic side-issues. What is the cost in predators of producing a game crop? Should we have further recourse to exotics? How can management restore the shrinking species, like prairie grouse, already hopeless as shootable game? How can management restore the threatened ratites, like trumpeter swan and whooping crane? Can management principles be extended to wildflowers? Here again it is clear to me that we have the same A-B cleavage as in forestry.

In the larger field of agriculture I am less competent to speak, but there seem to be somewhat parallel cleavages. Scientific agriculture was actively developing before ecology was born, hence a slower penetration of ecological concepts might be expected. Moreover the farmer, by the very nature of his techniques, must modify the biota more radically than the forester or the wildlife manager. Nevertheless, there are many discontents in agriculture which seem to add up to a new vision of 'biotic farming.'

Perhaps the most important of these is the new evidence that poundage or tonnage is no measure of the food-value of farm crops; the products of fertile soil may be qualitatively as well as quantitatively superior. We can bolster poundage from depleted soils by pouring on imported fertility, but we are not necessarily bolstering food-value. The possible ultimate ramifications of this idea are so immense that I must leave their exposition to abler pens.

The discontent that labels itself 'organic farming,' while bearing some of the earmarks of a cult, is nevertheless biotic in its direction, particularly in its insistence on the importance of soil flora and fauna.

The ecological fundamentals of agriculture are just as poorly known to the public as in other fields of land-use. For example, few educated people realize that the marvelous advances in technique made during recent decades are improvements in the pump, rather than the well. Acre for acre, they have barely sufficed to offset the sinking level of fertility.

In all of these cleavages, we see repeated the same basic paradoxes: man the conqueror *versus* man the biotic citizen; science the sharpener of his sword *versus* science the searchlight on his universe; land the slave and servant *versus* land the collective organism. Robinson's injunction to Tristram may well be applied, at this juncture, to *Homo sapiens* as a species in geological time:

> Whether you will or not
> You are a King, Tristram, for you are one
> Of the time-tested few that leave the world,
> When they are gone, not the same place it was.
> Mark what you leave.

The Outlook

It is inconceivable to me that an ethical relation to land can exist without love, respect, and admiration for land, and a high regard for its value. By value, I of course mean something far broader than mere economic value; I mean value in the philosophical sense.

Perhaps the most serious obstacle impeding the evolution of a land ethic is the fact that our educational and economic system is headed away from, rather than toward, an intense consciousness of land. Your true modern is separated from the land by many middlemen, and by innumerable physical gadgets. He has no vital relation to it; to him it is the space between cities on which crops grow. Turn him loose for a day on the land, and if the spot does not happen to be a golf links or a 'scenic' area, he is bored stiff. If crops could be raised by hydroponics instead of farming, it would suit him very well. Synthetic substitutes for wood, leather, wool, and other natural land products suit him better than the originals. In short, land is something he has 'outgrown.'

Almost equally serious as an obstacle to a land ethic is the attitude of the farmer for whom the land is still an adversary, or a taskmaster that keeps him in slavery. Theoretically, the mechanization of farming ought to cut the farmer's chains, but whether it really does is debatable.

One of the requisites for an ecological comprehension of land is an understanding of ecology, and this is by no means co-extensive with 'education'; in fact, much higher education seems deliberately to avoid ecological concepts. An understanding of ecology does not necessarily originate in courses bearing ecological labels; it is quite as likely to be labeled geography, botany, agronomy, history, or economics. This is as it should be, but whatever the label, ecological training is scarce.

The case for a land ethic would appear hopeless but for the minority which is in obvious revolt against these 'modern' trends.

The 'key-log' which must be moved to release the evolutionary process for an ethic is simply this: quit thinking about decent land-use as solely an economic problem. Examine each question in terms of what is ethically and esthetically right, as well as what is economically expedient. A thing is right when it tends to preserve the integrity, stability, and beauty of the biotic community. It is wrong when it tends otherwise.

It of course goes without saying that economic feasibility limits the tether of what can or cannot be done for land. It always has and it always will. The fallacy the economic determinists have tied around

our collective neck, and which we now need to cast off, is the belief that economics determines *all* land-use. This is simply not true. An innumerable host of actions and attitudes, comprising perhaps the bulk of all land relations, is determined by the land-users' tastes and predilections, rather than by his purse. The bulk of all land relations hinges on investments of time, forethought, skill, and faith rather than on investments of cash. As a land-user thinketh, so is he.

I have purposely presented the land ethic as a product of social evolution because nothing so important as an ethic is ever 'written.' Only the most superficial student of history supposes that Moses 'wrote' the Decalogue; it evolved in the minds of a thinking community, and Moses wrote a tentative summary of it for a 'seminar.' I say tentative because evolution never stops.

The evolution of a land ethic is an intellectual as well as emotional process. Conservation is paved with good intentions which prove to be futile, or even dangerous, because they are devoid of critical understanding either of the land, or of economic land-use. I think it is a truism that as the ethical frontier advances from the individual to the community, its intellectual content increases.

The mechanism of operation is the same for any ethic: social approbation for right actions: social disapproval for wrong actions.

By and large, our present problem is one of attitudes and implements. We are remodeling the Alhambra with a steam-shovel, and we are proud of our yardage. We shall hardly relinquish the shovel, which after all has many good points, but we are in need of gentler and more objective criteria for its successful use.

The Nature of the Everglades

Marjory Stoneman Douglas

Tʜᴇʀᴇ are no other Everglades in the world.

They are, they have always been, one of the unique regions of the earth, remote, never wholly known. Nothing anywhere else is like them: their vast glittering openness, wider than the enormous visible round of the horizon, the racing free saltness and sweetness of their massive winds, under the dazzling blue heights of space. They are unique also in the simplicity, the diversity, the related harmony of the forms of life they enclose. The miracle of the light pours over the green and brown expanse of saw grass and of water, shining and slow-moving below, the grass and water that is the meaning and the central fact of the Everglades of Florida. It is a river of grass.

The great pointed paw of the state of Florida, familiar as the map of North America itself, of which it is the most noticeable appendage, thrusts south, farther south than any other part of the mainland of the United States. Between the shining aquamarine waters of the Gulf of Mexico and the roaring deep-blue waters of the north-surging Gulf Stream, the shaped land points toward Cuba and the Caribbean. It points toward and touches within one degree of the tropics.

More than halfway down that thrusting sea-bound peninsula nearly everyone knows the lake that is like a great hole in that pawing shape, Lake Okeechobee, the second largest body of fresh water, it is always said, "within the confines of the United States." Below that lie the Everglades.

They have been called "the mysterious Everglades" so long that the phrase is a meaningless platitude. For four hundred years after the discovery they seemed more like a fantasy than a simple geographic and historic fact. Even the men who in the later years saw them more clearly could hardly make up their minds what the Everglades were or how they could be described, or what use could be made of them. They were mysterious then. They are mysterious still to everyone by whom their fundamental nature is not understood.

Off and on for those four hundred years the region now called "The Everglades" was described as a series of vast, miasmic swamps, poisonous lagoons, huge dismal marshes without outlet, a rotting, shallow, inland sea, or labyrinths of dark trees hung and looped about with snakes and dripping mosses, malignant with tropical fevers and malarias, evil to the white man.

Even the name, "The Everglades," was given them and printed on a map of Florida within the past hundred years. It is variously interpreted. There were one or two other names we know, which were given them before that, but what sounds the first men had for them, seeing first, centuries and centuries before the discovering white men, those sun-blazing solitudes, we shall never know.

The shores that surround the Everglades were the first on this continent known to white men. The interior was almost the last. They have not yet been entirely mapped.

Spanish mapmakers, who never saw them, printed over the unknown blank space where they lay on those early maps the words "El Laguno del Espiritu Santo." To the early Spanish they were truly mysterious, fabulous with a wealth they were never able to prove.

The English from the Bahamas, charting the Florida coasts in the early seventeen hundreds, had no very clear idea of them. Gerard de Brahm, the surveyor, may have gone up some of the east-coast rivers and stared out on that endless, watery bright expanse, for on his map he called them "River Glades." But on the later English maps "River" becomes "Ever," so it is hard to tell what he intended.

The present name came into general use only after the acquisition of Florida from Spain in 1819 by the United States. The Turner map of 1823 was the first to use the word "Everglades." The fine Ives map of 1856 prints the words separately, "Ever Glades." In the text of the memorial that accompanied the map they were used without capitals, as "ever glades."

The word "glade" is of the oldest English origin. It comes from the Anglo-Saxon "glaed," with the "ae" diphthong, shortened to "glad." It meant "shining" or "bright," perhaps as of water. The same word was used in the Scandinavian languages for "a clear place in the sky, a bright streak or patch of light," as Webster's International Dictionary gives it. It might even first have referred to the great openness of the sky over it, and not to the land at all.

In English for over a thousand years the word "glaed" or "glyde" or "glade" has meant an open green grassy place in the forest. And in America of the English colonies the use was continued to mean stretches of natural pasture, naturally grassy.

But most dictionaries nowadays end a definition of them with the qualifying phrase, "as of the Florida Everglades." So that they have thus become unique in being their own, and only, best definition.

Yet the Indians, who have known the Glades longer and better than any dictionary-making white men, gave them their perfect, and poetic name, which is also true. They called them "Pa-hay-okee," which is the Indian word for "Grassy Water." Today Everglades is one word and yet plural. They are the only Everglades in the world.

Men crossed and recrossed them leaving no trace, so that no one knew men had been there. The few books or pamphlets written about them by Spaniards or surveyors or sportsmen or botanists have not been generally read. Actually, the first accurate studies of Everglades geology, soil, archaeology, even history, are only just now being completed.

The question was at once, where do you begin? Because, when you think of it, history, the recorded time of the earth and of man, is in itself something like a river. To try to present it whole is to find oneself lost in the sense of continuing change. The source can be only the beginning in time and space, and the end is the future and the unknown. What we can know lies somewhere between. The course along which for a little way one proceeds, the changing life, the varying light, must somehow be fixed in a moment clearly, from which one may look before and after and try to comprehend wholeness.

So it is with the Everglades, which have that quality of long existence in their own nature. They were changeless. They are changed.

They were complete before man came to them, and for centuries afterward, when he was only one of those forms which shared, in a finely balanced harmony, the forces and the ancient nature of the place.

Then, when the Everglades were most truly themselves, is the time to begin with them.

II. THE GRASS

THE Everglades begin at Lake Okeechobee.

That is the name later Indians gave the lake, a name almost as recent as the word "Everglades." It means "Big Water." Everybody knows it.

Yet few have any idea of those pale, seemingly illimitable waters. Over the shallows, often less than a foot deep but seven hundred fifty or so square miles in actual area, the winds in one gray swift moment can shatter the reflections of sky and cloud whiteness standing still in that shining, polished, shimmering expanse. A boat can push for hours in a day of white sun through the short, crisp lake waves and there will be nothing to be seen anywhere but the brightness where the color of the water and the color of the sky become one. Men out of sight of land can stand in it up to their armpits and slowly "walk in" their long nets to the waiting boats. An everglade kite and his mate, questing in great solitary circles, rising and dipping and rising again on the wind currents, can look down all day long at the water faintly green with floating water lettuce or marked by thin standing lines of reeds, utter their sharp goat cries, and be seen and heard by no one at all.

There are great shallow islands, all brown reeds or shrubby trees thick in the water. There are masses of water weeds and hyacinths and flags rooted so long they seem solid earth, yet there is nothing but lake bottom to stand on. There the egret

and the white ibis and the glossy ibis and the little blue herons in their thousands nested and circled and fed.

A long northeast wind, a "norther," can lash all that still surface to dirty vicious gray and white, over which the rain mists shut down like stained rolls of wool, so that from the eastern sand rim under dripping cypresses or the west ridge with its live oaks, no one would guess that all that waste of empty water stretched there but for the long monotonous wash of waves on unseen marshy shores.

Saw grass reaches up both sides of that lake in great enclosing arms, so that it is correct to say that the Everglades are there also. But south, southeast and southwest, where the lake water slopped and seeped and ran over and under the rock and soil, the greatest mass of the saw grass begins. It stretches as it always has stretched, in one thick enormous curving river of grass, to the very end. This is the Everglades.

It reaches one hundred miles from Lake Okeechobee to the Gulf of Mexico, fifty, sixty, even seventy miles wide. No one has ever fought his way along its full length. Few have ever crossed the northern wilderness of nothing but grass. Down that almost invisible slope the water moves. The grass stands. Where the grass and the water are there is the heart, the current, the meaning of the Everglades.

The grass and the water together make the river as simple as it is unique. There is no other river like it. Yet within that simplicity, enclosed within the river and bordering and intruding on it from each side, there is subtlety and diversity, a crowd of changing forms, of thrusting teeming life. And all that becomes the region of the Everglades.

The truth of the river is the grass. They call it saw grass. Yet in the botanical sense it is not grass at all so much as a fierce, ancient, cutting sedge. It is one of the oldest of the green growing forms in this world.

There are many places in the South where this saw grass,

with its sharp central fold and edges set with fine saw teeth like points of glass, this sedge called *Cladium jamaicensis*, exists. But this is the greatest concentration of saw grass in the world. It grows fiercely in the fresh water creeping down below it. When the original saw grass thrust up its spears into the sun, the fierce sun, lord and power and first cause over the Everglades as of all the green world, then the Everglades began. They lie wherever the saw grass extends: 3,500 square miles, hundreds and thousands and millions, of acres, water and saw grass.

The first saw grass, exactly as it grows today, sprang up and lived in the sweet water and the pouring sunlight, and died in it, and from its own dried and decaying tissues and tough fibers bright with silica sprang up more fiercely again. Year after year it grew and was fed by its own brown rotting, taller and denser in the dark soil of its own death. Year after year after year, hundreds after hundreds of years, not so long as any geologic age but long in botanic time, far longer than anyone can be sure of, the saw grass grew. Four thousand years, they say, it must at least have grown like that, six feet, ten feet, twelve feet, even fifteen in places of deepest water. The edged and folded swords bristled around the delicate straight tube of pith that burst into brown flowering. The brown seed, tight enclosed after the manner of sedges, ripened in dense brownness. The seed was dropped and worked down in the water and its own ropelike mat of roots. All that decay of leaves and seed covers and roots was packed deeper year after year by the elbowing upthrust of its own life. Year after year it laid down new layers of virgin muck under the living water.

There are places now where the depth of the muck is equal to the height of the saw grass. When it is uncovered and brought into the sunlight, its stringy and grainy dullness glitters with the myriad unrotted silica points, like glass dust.

At the edges of the Glades, and toward those southern- and southwesternmost reaches where the great estuary or delta of the Glades river takes another form entirely, the saw grass is shorter and more sparse, and the springy, porous muck deposit under it is shallower and thinner. But where the saw grass grows tallest in the deepest muck, there goes the channel of the Glades.

The water winks and flashes here and there among the saw-grass roots, as the clouds are blown across the sun. To try to make one's way among these impenetrable tufts is to be cut off from all air, to be beaten down by the sun and ripped by the grassy saw-toothed edges as one sinks in mud and water over the roots. The dried yellow stuff holds no weight. There is no earthly way to get through the mud or the standing, keen-edged blades that crowd these interminable miles.

Or in the times of high water in the old days, the flood would rise until the highest tops of that sharp grass were like a thin lawn standing out of water as blue as the sky, rippling and wrinkling, linking the pools and spreading and flowing on its true course southward.

A man standing in the center of it, if he could get there, would be as lost in saw grass, as out of sight of anything but saw grass as a man drowning in the middle of Okeechobee—or the Atlantic Ocean, for that matter—would be out of sight of land.

The water moves. The saw grass, pale green to deep-brown ripeness, stands rigid. It is moved only in sluggish rollings by the vast push of the winds across it. Over its endless acres here and there the shadows of the dazzling clouds quicken and slide, purple-brown, plum-brown, mauve-brown, rust-brown, bronze. The bristling, blossoming tops do not bend easily like standing grain. They do not even in their own growth curve all one way but stand in edged clumps, curving against each other, all the massed curving blades making millions of fine arching lines that at a little distance merge to a huge expanse of brown wires or bristles or, farther beyond, to deep-piled plush. At the horizon they become velvet. The line they make is an edge of velvet against the infinite blue, the blue-and-white, the clear fine primrose yellow, the burning brass and crimson, the molten silver, the deepening hyacinth sky.

The clear burning light of the sun pours daylong into the saw grass and is lost there, soaked up, never given back. Only the water flashes and glints. The grass yields nothing.

Nothing less than the smashing power of some hurricane can beat it down. Then one can see, from high up in a plane, where the towering weight and velocity of the hurricane was the strongest and where along the edges of its whorl it turned less and less savagely and left the saw grass standing. Even so, the grass is not flattened in a continuous swath but only here and here and over there, as if the storm bounced or lifted and smashed down again in great hammering strokes or enormous cat-licks.

Only one force can conquer it completely and that is fire. Deep in the layers of muck there are layers of ashes, marks of old fires set by lightning or the early Indians. But in the early days the water always came back and there were long slow years in which the saw grass grew and died, laying down again its tough resilient decay.

This is the saw grass, then, which seems to move as the water moved, in a great thick arc south and southwestward from Okeechobee to the Gulf. There at the last imperceptible incline of the land the saw grass goes along the headwaters of many of those wide, slow, mangrove-bordered fresh-water rivers, like a delta or an estuary into which the salt tides flow and draw back and flow again.

The mangrove becomes a solid barrier there, which by its strong, arched and labyrinthine roots collects the sweepage of the fresh water and the salt and holds back the parent sea. The supple branches, the oily green leaves, set up a barrier against the winds, although the hurricanes prevail easily against them. There the fresh water meets the incoming salt, and is lost.

It may be that the mystery of the Everglades is the saw grass, so simple, so enduring, so hostile. It was the saw grass and the water which divided east coast from west coast and made the central solitudes that held in them the secrets of time, which has moved here so long unmarked.

III. THE WATER

In the Everglades one is most aware of the superb monotony of saw grass under the world of air. But below that and before it, enclosing and causing it, is the water.

It is poured into Lake Okeechobee from the north and west, from that fine chain of lakes which scatter up and down the center of Florida, like bright beads from a string. They overflow southward. The water is gathered from the northwest through a wide area of open savannas and prairies. It swells the greatest contributing streams, the Kissimmee River, and the Taylor River and Fisheating Creek, and dozens of other smaller named and unnamed creeks or rivulets, and through them moves down into the great lake's tideless blue-misted expanse.

The water comes from the rains. The northern lakes and streams, Okeechobee itself, are only channels and reservoirs and conduits for a surface flow of rain water, fresh from the clouds. A few springs may feed them, but no melting snow water, no mountain freshets, no upgushing from caverns in ancient rock. Here the rain is everything.

Here the rain falls more powerfully and logically than anywhere else upon the temperate mainland of the United States.

There are not four sharply marked seasons, as in the North. Here winter and spring and summer and fall blend into each other subtly, with nothing like such extremes of heat and cold. Here, actually, there are only two seasons, the wet and the dry, as there are in the tropics. The rains thunder over all this long land in their appointed season from the low clouds blowing in from the sea, or pour from clouds gathered all morning from the condensation of the wet below. Then for months it will not rain at all, or very little, and the high sun glares over the drying saw grass and the river seems to stand still.

This land, by the maps, is in the temperate zone. But the laws of the rain and of the seasons here are tropic laws.

The men who make maps draw lines across seas and deserts and mountains and equatorial rain forests to show where the Temperate Zone is cut off sharply from the middle equatorial belt. But the sea and the land and the winds do not always recognize that rigidity. Nor do southern Florida and the Everglades.

To the west the map shows the Gulf of Mexico, that warm land-sheltered, almost inland ocean; and from it, moved by the power of the turning world itself, the Gulf Stream pours its warm deep indigo and white-flecked waters north of Cuba and ever northeastward. "The Stream" is a huge swift-running river of warm salt water forced between the Florida coast, which it has shaped, and the Bahama banks, until high up on the blue globe of ocean it swings far across into the gray latitudes, toward frozen seas.

With all that surrounding warm sea water and not forgetting Okeechobee's over seven hundred shallow watery square miles, east forty miles from the sea, and from the Gulf eighty, the whole southern part of Florida might as well be an island. All summer long the trade winds, or winds blowing so steadily nightlong and daylong from the southeast that it makes no

difference if weather men quarrel about their being called the true trades, pour across the land their cool stiff tides of ten miles an hour.

Summer and winter its climate is more equable than that of the mainland regions to the north. And because of its average sixty-five inches a year of rainfall on the east coast and sixty-three in the interior of the Everglades, this region actually resembles certain warm and rainy but not too hot tropic lands more than it does those other dry and mountainous countries which lie exactly on the equator. It is a question of the ratio between the temperature and the rainfall and the evaporation. There is an arc at the very tip of Florida, up the lower west coast to Gordon Pass and up the east coast to the Miami and New rivers, which is the only place on the mainland of the United States where tropical and West Indian plants will grow native, because of that warmth and rainfall.

The northern Glades, and Lake Okeechobee, would seem to be in the South Temperate Zone, but the rainfall is subtropic here too.

The rains begin in the spring, in April or even late in May. There may be a few days of stuffy wet heat and brassy sunlight and a great piling up and movement of clouds by the heavy fretful southeast winds. There may be a continuous bumping of thunder far off. The winds that change their compass positions, east to south to west to north to east again, never on the east and south coasts, in any other way but clockwise, are thrashing and uncertain. Then in a sudden chill the rain may shut down in one long slashing burst in which even hailstones may bounce like popcorn against all that darkening land. Then the rain has moved away and the sun flashes again.

Somewhere thereafter it rains over the Glades or the lake for an hour or two every day in switching long bright lines through which the hot sun glistens. Then the marching wet will start again the next day or so, hissing and leaping down in narrow sharply defined paths as the clouds are pushed about here and there in the bright sky. Sometimes the rains may last only a few weeks in May. After that the summer is a long blazing drying time of brilliant sun and trade winds all night under the steady wheeling of the stars. The great piles of vapor from the Gulf Stream, amazing cumulus clouds that soar higher than tropic mountains from their even bases four thousand feet above the horizon, stand in ranked and glistening splendor in those summer nights; twenty thousand feet or more they tower tremendous, cool-pearl, frosty heights, blue-shadowed in the blue-blazing days.

On summer mornings over the Glades the sky is only faintly hazed. The moisture is being drawn up from the sheen among the saw grass. By noon, the first ranks of the clouds will lie at the same height across the world, cottony and growing. The moisture lifts the whipped and glistening heights. The bases darken, grow purple, grow brown. The sun is almost gone. The highest clouds loose their moisture, which is condensed into cloud again before it can reach the earth. Then they grow more heavy. The winds slash before them and the rains roar down, making all the saw grass somber.

Sometimes the rainy season goes on all summer, casually raining here and there so that the green things never quite dry out while salt-water mosquitoes from the brackish pools about the coasts blow on the west wind in thin screaming hordes. When high water in the Glades flows south, the mosquitoes do not breed in it.

But in late August, or perhaps in September, the rainy season sets in in earnest. White-heaped Gulf clouds, colored by afterglows in some tremendous summer sunsets stand like Alps of pure rose and violet and ice-gray against the ultimate blue until they are harried by the more irregular winds. White

streamers are blown from their tops, veils from their sides, and they themselves are pushed and scuffled and beaten down into long moving snowy sheets or rolls of gray, yellowish-gray, lavender-gray, greenish-gray—until they smash down in long marching, continuous, reverberating downfalls.

You can see it raining darkly and fiercely far off over there at the horizon across the scorched saw grass. The sky will be a boiling panorama of high and low cloud shapes, cumulus, strato-cumulus, alto-cumulus, dazzling and blue and dun. Sometimes far up, far away, between all that panoply, there will be a glimpse of outer space as green as ice.

Then the lion-colored light shuts down as the rain does, or the clouds fill with their steely haze every outline of the visible world and water falls solid, in sheets, in cascades. When the clouds lift, the long straight rainy lines blow and curve from the sagging underbelly of the sky in steely wires or long trailing veils of wet that glitter in some sudden shaft of light from the forgotten sun.

There will be the smack of cool, almost chilling hard air and the rising sound of long drumming as if the grassy places were hard and dry, or the earth hollow. You hear the tearing swish of the rain on the stiff saw grass as it comes over and beats and goes by slashing its steely whips. There may be short bursts of thunder and veins of lightning cracking the whole sky. They are dwarfed by the power of the rain and the wind.

Below all that the glistening water will be rising, shining like beaten pewter, and the light will lift as if itself relieved of all that weight of the rain. It will change from pewter to silver to pure brightness everywhere. The brownness that has been dullness will be bright tawniness and the reaches and changing forms of the sky will lift higher and higher, lifting the heart. Suddenly all those thousands and thousands of acres of saw grass that have been so lightless and somber will burst into a million million flashes from as many gleaming and trembling drops of wet, flashing back their red and emerald and diamond lights to the revealed glory of the sun in splendor.

Inches of water will have fallen in an hour and still far off the rain will trample below the horizon, undiminished.

In the course of a single day so much rain will fall, as much sometimes as ten or twelve inches, that the glitter of rising water will be everywhere. The blue of the sky is caught down there among the grass stems, in pools stretching and spreading. In a few days of rain, acre after acre of new water will flash in sheets under the sun. Then, as the rain clouds go over every day, the currents will be gathering their small visible courses, streaming and swirling past every grass blade, moving south and again south and by west. Places of open currents have been measured to show a steady running four miles an hour, in the old days, in watercourses and wandering streams among the straight bristle of the saw grass. Sometimes more than half the year's average will have fallen in less than two months.

Meanwhile the rain has been falling far to the northward. Over Okeechobee it has been moved here and there as the steady drive of the trades is changed to fitful inland airs. Thunderstorms roll and reverberate over the surface and lightning marbles the clouds as storms seem to come together from every direction while the greenish and grayish world blinks with acid radiance. The lake may be blotted out by white falling water that sings with a rising note as the surface brims and is beaten. The curtains of rain, the rain fogs, move off or hang and sway in a dirty gray half-light as the descending water smacks on the pitted and broken waves. The world is all water, is drowned in water, chill and pale and clean.

North, still farther up that chain of lakes, the rains fall and brim the fine green-ringed cups. The waters begin again their southward flow. The Kissimmee River is swollen and strongly swirling between its wet marshy banks, but still the water does not move off fast enough. The banks are overflowing and the spongy ground between it and Fisheating Creek is all one swamp. The rains fling their solid shafts of water down the streaming green land, and Okeechobee swells and stirs and creeps south down the unseen tilt of the Glades.

The grass, like all the other growing things after the long terrible dry seasons, begins in the flooding wet its strong sunward push again, from its ropy roots. The spears prick upward, tender green, glass green, bright green, darker green, to spread the blossoms and the fine seeds like brown lace. The grass stays. The fresh river flows.

But even from earliest times, when in the creeping spread of water the grass turned up its swords and made the Everglades, there was too much water in the great lake to carry itself off through the Glades southward. There was nothing but the east and west sandy ridges to hold back the water. To the east from Okeechobee it seeped and was not carried off and stood along an old wandering watercourse soon filled not only with saw grass but reeds and sedges and purple arrowy lilies and floating masses of grass and small trees. That is still called the Loxahatchee Slough. "Hatchee" means "river" in that same Indian tongue which named the lake. "Slough," in south Florida, means any open swampy place which may once have been a tongue of the sea or a river of fresh water, green, watery, flowery country, a place of herons and small fish and dragonflies and blue sky flashing from among the lily pads.

Loxahatchee is pitted with innumerable pools held in by the coastal rock. South of that, from the overflow of the Glades basin itself, the rivers of the east coast run, St. Lucie and the Hillsborough, the New River and Little River and the Miami River, spilling over the rock rim to the tides.

In the same way, west of Lake Okeechobee, at least twice

as far from the Gulf, the water spilled and crept out over soggy level lands, half lakes, half swamps, and so into the Caloosahatchee, the left shoulder of the Glades region.

The Caloosahatchee never rose directly in Okeechobee, but in a wide rain-filled funnel of shallow, grassy lakes between Hicpochee and Lake Flirt. Often they dried up and were not there.

West of Lake Flirt, the Caloosahatchee began in earnest, a river so remote, so lovely that even in the days when it was best known it must have been like a dream. It was a river wandering among half-moon banks hung with green dripping trees and enshrouding grapevines, green misted, silent, always meandering. It has that quality of dreaming still, neglected and changed as it is, to this very day.

But in the days of full flood, Caloosahatchee rose and overflowed the flat country for miles, north and south. The water crept and flowed and stood bright under the high water oaks and the cabbage palms, so that a light boat could go anywhere under them. In the clear water all the light under the wet trees was green. Lower down, the more tropic green stood in solid jungles to the reflecting water. The rain water went east and west of the lake, but most strongly along the great course of the Everglades.

Often the rainy season finds its terrible climax in September or October, in the crashing impact of a hurricane, the true cyclonic storm of the tropics. July is not too early to expect hurricanes. In the West Indies they have occurred in June. The old jingle that fishermen recite along these coasts tells the story: "June—too soon. July—stand by. August—look out you must. September—remember. October—all over." Officially in Florida the fifteenth of November closes the hurricane season but farther south these storms occur in November and even in December.

The hurricanes make up, although no man has yet seen the actual beginning of one, as far east as the Azores, where the hot air rises all along the line of the equator as the Northern Hemisphere cools toward winter. Their enormous high-spinning funnels, moving always counterclockwise this north side of the tropic belt, are begun when the rising hot air is flung into circular motion by the immeasurable spinning power of the world. The velocity of that spin around their hollow centers has been recorded as moving as fast as two hundred miles. But generally the recording instruments are blown away before that, so no one knows their greatest speed. Laterally, they creep westward more slowly, ten to forty miles an hour. They enter the Caribbean at some airy rift between those island-mountains rising from the sea, which are often engulfed by them. They may turn northward and eastward through the Mona or the Windward Passage, or across the Cuban coast or through the Bahamas, to drive on southern Florida. They may go howling up these coasts and north along, to show the Temperate Zone what the roused raging power of the tropics can be like.

Smaller but intense and dangerous hurricanes spring up sometimes in the late fall in the Yucatan channel and thrash the Gulf of Mexico and harry the Texas or Florida coast. They attack the Glades from there. Later still, they become more freakish and unpredictable, like maelstroms of wind gone wild.

But as the northern winter creeps downward, the hurricane season is slowly conquered. The towering clouds of summer are leveled to mild sheets and rolls of gleaming stuff, widespread, dappled and mackereled, or with the great silvery brushings of mares'-tails. Often there are no clouds at all toward the zenith, which has lost its summer intensity of violet and burns now with the bright crisp blue of northern autumns. Then the air is fresh and sweet.

This is the dry season. Officially, no rain should fall. Yet there have been wet, chill winters in which the rains have come down on the edge of a northern cold front while the east winds go around south and west and north, and stand there for three days of cold, or die utterly so that the frost drifts into the low places and at first sun the hoar-rimmed leaves grow black.

In the winter dry season, there takes place here another and gentler phenomenon of the equatorial tropics. In a windless dawn, in some light winter ground fogs, in mists that stand over the Everglades watercourses, the dew creeps like heavy rain down the shining heavy leaves, drips from the saw-grass edges, and stands among the coarse blossoming sedges and the tall ferns. Under the tree branches it is a steady soft drop, drop and drip, all night long. In the first sunlight the dew, a miracle of freshness, stands on every leaf and wall and petal, in the finest of tiny patterns, in bold patterns of wide-strung cobwebs; like pearls in a silvery melting frostwork. The slant yellow sun of winter dries it up in the next hour but all the secret roots are nourished by it in the dry ground.

Then toward what the North would call spring, dryness creeps again over the land, with the high-standing sun. Between one day and the next the winds grow new and powerful. In the Glades the water shrinks below the grass roots. In open muddy places far south the surface dries and cracks like the cracks in old china, and where some alligator has hitched his slow armored length from one drying water hole to another the pattern of his sharp toes and heavy dragging belly in the marl is baked hard.

The saw grass stands drying to old gold and rustling faintly, ready, if there is a spark anywhere, to burst into those boiling red flames which crackle even at a great distance like a vast frying pan, giving off rolling clouds of heavy cream-colored smoke, shadowed with mauve by day and by night mile-high

pillars of roily tangerine and orange light. The fires move crackling outward as the winds blow them, black widening rings where slow embers burn and smolder down into the fibrous masses of the thousand-year-old peat.

Then the spring rains put out the fires with their light moving tread, like the tread of the running deer, and the year of rainy season and of dry season has made its round again.

"Look where the sun draws up water," people say of those long shafts of brightness between clouds. The saw grass and all those acres of green growing things draw up the water within their cells and use it and breathe it out again, invisibly. Transpiration and evaporation, it is called; an unending usage of all the water that has fallen and that flows. Sixty per cent of it, over half of all those tons and tons of water which fall in any rainy season, is taken up again. Dried up. The air is fresh with it, or humid, if it is warm. But in the middle of the Glades in the full heat of summer the condensation is so great that the air is cooled and the temperature lowered half a degree with every two miles or so inland. It is not so much the cool movement of wind as standing coolness, freshness without salt, wetness that is sweet with the breath of hidden tiny blossoming things luminous in the darkness under the height and white magnificence of the stars. Such coolness is a secret that the deep Glades hold.

On the west coast there are land breezes and sea breezes. West-flowing winds often sweep out of those cooling Glades down the slow mangrove rivers and out to the islands on the coasts, rivers of coolness among warm and standing airs.

With all this, it is the subtle ratio between rainfall and evaporation that is the final secret of water in the Glades. We must know a great deal more about that ratio and its effect on temperature in all this region to understand its influence on the weather, on frosts and winds and storms.

All this has been caused by other cycles dictated by remote and terrible occurrences beyond this infinitesimal world, the cyclones of heat and shadow that pass across the utter fire of the sun. Or other laws of a universe only half guessed at. Those majestic affairs reach here in long cycles of alternating wet and dry. There have been years after years of long rainy seasons when the Glades indeed were a running river, more water than grass. Or, more recently, cycles of drought, when there is never enough rain to equal the evaporation and transpiration and the runoff.

Because of all this, the high rate of water usage as against the natural runoff, it is clear that rainfall alone could not have maintained the persistent fine balance between wet and dry that has created and kept the Everglades, the long heart of this long land. If Okeechobee and the lakes and marshes north that contribute to it, if rivers and swamps and ponds had not existed to hoard all that excess water in a great series of reservoirs by which the flow was constantly checked and regulated, there would have been no Everglades. The whole system was like a set of scales on which the forces of the seasons, of the sun and the rains, the winds, the hurricanes, and the dewfalls, were balanced so that the life of the vast grass and all its encompassed and neighbor forms were kept secure.

Below all that, holding all that, the foundation stuff of this world, lies the rock.

IV. THE ROCK

To understand the Everglades one must first understand the rock.

The outline of this Florida end-of-land, within the Gulf of Mexico, the shallows of the Bay of Florida and the Gulf Stream, is like a long pointed spoon. That is the visible shape of the rock that holds up out of the surrounding sea water the long channel of the Everglades and their borders. The rock holds the fresh water and the grass and all those other shapes and forms of air-loving life only a little way out of the salt water, as a full spoon lowered into a full cup holds two liquids separate, within that thread of rim. Lower the tip of the spoon a very little and the higher liquid moves out across the submerged end, as the water does at the end of the Glades.

The rock beneath Okeechobee is only a few feet above sea level. The surface of the lake is only twenty-one feet above the level of the salt water. The surface rock below the Everglades dips south at an incline of half a foot to every six miles. The rim of rock that retains it is narrower and higher on the east coast, but in the west it is hardly visible as a rim at all. There it is a broad space of inland swamps and prairies and coastal sandy land and salt-invaded marshes. Yet both hold against the sea.

The rock is not by any means the oldest in the world. It is nothing like the perdurable granite of the ancient Appalachian spine of the eastern continent. The material of it came from the sea. Out of reach of air it is lumpy, soft, permeable limestone, grayish white, unformed. They call it "oölitic limestone" because it is no more fused together than a lot of fish eggs. In the sun and air it hardens in clumps and shapeless masses, dark, or gray, or yellowish, all full of holes, pitted and pocked like lumps of rotting honeycomb. In itself it shows no foldings or stratification, but holds streaks of sand or shells or pockets of humus.

West and east of Okeechobee the rock just below the surface is not so much oölitic limestone as a shelly, marly sandstone. To the east it underlies the Loxahatchee Slough. To the west, under the swamps and flat ponds beyond Okeechobee, the

Caloosahatchee ran strong after the rains, turning from bank to bank in its overflow, carving its way across and into that sandstone plain in the meanders which are the habit of much older rivers. The Caloosahatchee is not so old as that river of Troy which was first called "Meander," but in her curvings and turnings she cut down through new sand into older and older layers of rock and of pure shell fossils. Some of the greatest layers of fossil shells in the world were cut into and crumbled, and cut into again as every year Caloosahatchee changed her banks.

In spite of what the early scientists believed, and people still repeat incorrectly to this day, this lower Florida is not an old coral reef. It is oölitic limestone, with broken bits of staghorn coral or shapes of brain coral embedded in it. "Miami limestone," they call it.

The fresh water from Okeechobee moving south on the long course of the Everglades has in these thousands of years worn the soft rock in a broad longitudinally grooved valley. Along the east coast the rock rim may be seen in long south-curving ledges, worn by the action of the sea. The rock rims emerge farther south still as beaches and peninsulas beyond half-enclosed salt rivers and broad opening bays. East, the sunken reefs stretch to the abrupt edge of the Gulf Stream itself, where the brilliant lime-green, surfless shallows drop off into the blue, deep surge.

South of the last peninsula, which makes Biscayne Bay, the ridges stretch below water to make the long spiny curves of the Florida Keys, turning southwest as the Gulf Stream came, all the way to Key West and the last Tortugas. Other lesser known rims of rock curve within the southeast mainland in a line of high rocky islands. These are called the Everglades Keys. They became legendary. The early white people believed they contained caves into which all the Indians disappeared before hurricanes, warned by the "blossoming of the saw grass," as if

the saw grass did not blossom every year, and as if the broken ledges of rock in these inland keys could hide anything except ferns and coral snakes and roots.

On the east coast, the rivers from the great main saw-grass stream broke through the rock rim in a series of low waterfalls or rapids. The rock stood as a constant natural dam between the fresh water of the Glades and the heavier invading tidal salt, which in dry times creeps up the bottoms of the rivers and would destroy all living fresh-water forms above the mangrove line.

The St. Lucie and the rivers running into Jupiter Inlet and the Mouth of the Rat, the Hillsborough, the New River with its two branches, Little River and Arch Creek, had their shallow falls. The Miami River from the Everglades brawled over twenty-five feet of rapids in the North Fork, with a fall of over six feet. Snapper Creek had its ferny, rocky dam, above which the fresh-water springs bubbled clear through all the higher rock.

The water of all these rivers was clean and clear, perhaps faintly brown from mangroves, but with no Everglades humus in it to stain the bright sand bottoms. The water of the bays was clear, tinted by the light shimmering in water over sand reefs, and sea gardens, and acres of clean green weed.

All that rocky barrier in fact was threaded with springs. All these rivers were known to the early sailors as "sweet water rivers," not a name but a description. The springs bubbled up and filled the great ancient pot holes in the rock which the sea had whirled into and worn smooth and deserted, thousands of years before.

The limestone tips very gently downward to the south until at the end it disappears below the surface and is overlaid by a fine, white calcareous marl that muffles all the shallow water of the Bay of Florida. There are blown sand beaches at Cape

Sable, the French word for "sand." There are deposits of leafy humus here and there over the marly meadows, and brackish lakes are set like mirrors among the mangroves, and the wandering watercourses are more salt than fresh. It is a marl laid down by infinitesimal algae. There are bits of seashells in it, bleached by the sun and abraded by the tides. The ripple shadows in the marly water are blue, in a liquid like thin cream. To wade out into it is to sink to the hips in ooze, in faintly scratchy white mud, warm as warm milk in the sun-warmed sea water over it.

All this end of the peninsula is a country that the sea has conquered and has never left. Beyond, westward, it is a pattern of curved shapes solid with mangroves cut out by salt water. There, from Cape Sable northward again to the lonely point of Cape Romano, lie the Ten Thousand Islands. They are the sunken tops of sand dunes the winds and the hurricanes piled up from the shallower Gulf. The mangrove covered them. They are edged on the west by fine, hard white sand beaches that are changed in shape with every hurricane. The passes become filled with sand that the mangroves and salt shrubs hurry to make solid, and then new passes are cut swiftly where the driven salt water rages.

On this coast, south of Cape Romano, the rivers move silent and enormous from the saw grass to the mangrove, and so to the sea, linked by innumerable streams and cuts and channels, utterly bewildering, never completely known. The fresh-water Turner River comes down from pineland and cypress to a dozen channels among mangroves, and so to Chokoloskee Bay. Chatham Bend opens out of Chevalier Bay like a great inland brackish lake. Some rivers above the tides are fresh water from the Everglades, many channeled and intricate; Lostman's River with its sand bars into the Gulf and Rodger's River and Harney's River. Then with impressive opening and far inward

reaching among saw-grass plains, there is the Broad River known only to the multitudinous flights of the birds at sunrise and sunset, crammed with fish, and once boiling with crocodiles; at noons it lies glaring, soundless, solitary, untouched. South of that is Shark River carved in the rock, and the Little Shark in all their branchings and windings among mangroves, opening inland in channels that lead behind the three capes of Cape Sable, more inlets than rivers, lakes, lagoons, all sun struck, sea invaded.

For the retaining shape of the rock that holds in the western curve of the saw-grass river, one has to go back to the cape and the angle that Caloosahatchee makes with it, a rough right angle, subtended by the long line of the outer coast. Up in that angle, as if it was the western armpit of that country, there is an unseen dome of limestone which makes a watershed for all this. It is not the edge of the true Glades, but it shows where the rock lies nearest to the surface, about at the place now called Immokalee. Water in the rains runs north to Caloosahatchee; west to the seacoast, in some of those small rivers like the Estero and the Imperial, once called Surveyor's Creek, and the Corkscrew River, and into Trafford Lake and Deep Lake, and others. Blue water stands in deep, round cups of the rock. East lies a strange country that borders the Glades sharply. The northern part is called the Devil's Garden, a broken scrubby open land. South is the mass of the Big Cypress, by which for a long time the saw grass curves.

All this again is drained by a bright green swampy, grassy trough called the Okaloacochee Slough, which leads southwestward into the Fakahatchee Swamp, half salt marshes and fresh water, which leads in turn into Fakahatchee Bay behind the mounded islands above the Allen, now the Barron, River.

So, in the middle of the narrow east coast and the broader west coast, the Everglades curve grandly in the limestone.

The rock is still strange stuff. The fresh Glades water wore it horizontally from north to southwest in a long valley, never smooth, but a series of long uneven ridges and troughs that hold the muck and the southernmost marl. It was porous stuff to begin with. And then all that fresh water wore and seeped down into it through the cloaking vegetable decay, charged with the strong organic acids that ate and gnawed and dissolved chemically the penetrable limestone. The acid water worked and tunneled it, so that it is honeycombed and fretted and pocked, under the layers of the muck, into something very like rocky sponge. All but the hardest cores and spines of limestone were eaten out downward many feet below the surface in an infinity of grooved strange shapes.

If all the saw grass and the peat was burned away there would be exposed to the sun glare the weirdest country in the world, thousands and hundreds of thousands of acres of fantastic rockwork, whity gray and yellow, streaked and blackened, pinnacles and domes and warped pyramids and crumbling columns and stalagmites, ridgy arches and half-exposed horizontal caverns, long downward cracks, and a million extraordinary chimney pots. Under the sun glare or the moonlight it would look stranger than a blasted volcano crater, or a landscape of the dead and eroded moon.

Nothing of that limestone shows above the surface in the northernmost Glades. For sixty miles or so south of Lake Okeechobee the river of the saw grass sweeps wider than the horizon, nothing but saw grass utterly level to the eye, a vast unbroken monotony. The grass crowds all across the visible width and rondure of the earth, like close-fitting fur. Clouds and the smoke of fires stand far off and are sunk in it, like the smoke of ships at sea. This is the Everglades at their greatest concentration, a world of nothing but saw grass. Nothing seems to live here but a few insects, hawks working a few acres, buzzards soaring

against the piled snow of a cloud, a heron flying its far solitary line.

The saw grass sweeps about halfway south, where the whole course begins to arc a little to the westward. There the muck is not so deep, less solidly packed over the limestone. The hardest rock began to show at the surface its ridged top in hundreds and thousands of places. In times of drought the soil subsided around this rock which the new rains and the suns eroded and wore off level. And the surface water around the exposed rock under the surrounding grass shaped and pointed it in the direction of the currents in islands like anchored ships swinging all in the same direction, fleets, flotillas, armadas of stranded island shapes. Southward the islands crowd more thickly in the thinning muck.

Plants seized upon these rocks, hardly less avidly than the saw grass, carried by wind or birds or water, and needing only a pinch of humus, some cranny more hospitable than the all-choking saw grass, in which to send down their first threadlike roots. The enormous machinery of the sun drew up the sprouts, the stalks, the trunks of trees, the covering leaves. Every island, almost at once, reached a tropical struggling life in blossom and quick seed.

These islands are, like the saw grass, the particular feature of the Glades. Small or great jungles, they loom out of the brownness of the saw grass in humped solid shapes, like green whales and gray-green hangars and domes and green clouds on the horizon. They look like hummocks, and many books persist in calling them so. They are called also "heads" and "strands" and "tree islands," but the right name is "hammock," from "hamaca," an Arawak word for jungle or masses of vegetation floating in a tropical river. These are the hammocks of the saw-grass river. No man has explored all of them, or could. They are too many. From north to south there is a changing vegetation on them, by which they can be characterized. Some have known history such as men make. Some hide marks of deeds that few men remember. Some have not known one single human thing, only the beasts and snakes and birds and insects that know nothing else since their time began.

That is not all, for this rock has a shape greater than this visible one of the peninsula. Westward it makes a great shadowy sunken plateau extending far out into the Gulf of Mexico in shallows that drop off abruptly into the midmost deeps. On the east coast it is gouged deeply by a stream of warm water over one of cold, with a current greater than the Mississippi that separates the American continent here at Florida from the Bahama Banks, two hundred fathoms deep, moving four to five miles an hour. It is the enormous oceanic river of the Gulf Stream.

The whole structure of this rock is known as the Floridian plateau. Still, to understand it, one must know how it was made, in time's forward-pushing inexorable years.

V. THE RIVER OF TIME

The life and death of the saw grass is only a moment of that flow in which time, the vastest river, carries us and all life forward. The water is timeless, forever new and eternal. Only the rock, which time shaped and will outlast, records unimaginable ages.

Yet, as time goes, this limestone is recent. The earth itself is so much older that time grows faint about it, in those hundreds of millions of years which, in its cooling and wrinkling and rising and wearing and changing, might have been but a single day. The mind of man has no way of holding so vast a concept. He has devised symbols to spare himself the agony of trying to think what that awfulness was like.

The earth was shrunken and old, the continents almost as we know them, already split and re-formed and taking shape within the all-encompassing ocean, when the Floridian plateau was still a part of the floor of a warm, tranquil, equatorial sea. The Appalachian Mountains to the north already had been thrust up and worn down again by the friction of centuries and still the sea lay here, wrinkling and glittering in its moon-enchanted tides. There was a stump at the south of that continental mass like the beginning of north Florida. Or perhaps it was an island. But that was all.

There came one last heaving and changing, some huge undersea faulting and pinching up, and in long slow centuries the Floridian plateau rose a little, only a little, the east edge of it a little higher, the west sloping back gradually to the sea again. The sea water ran off it as if it were the rising shoulder of some huge sleek beast. The ridged shelly oozy bottom of the sea broke into the sunlight for the first time and as the waters within what we now call the Gulf of Mexico felt the narrowing pinch of the land, they began to pour out irresistibly, as the earth turned, in the Gulf Stream.

They say that was late in the earth's history, a mere geologic yesterday. The Pliocene, they call it, which is only a way of bunching together an unbelievable section of centuries in one word that can be handled without too much thought. They think it was nineteen million years ago and that the period lasted millions of years.

Life had taken shape on the earth long before, long, long before, the top of this Florida rock rose above the sea. Shapes of growing things which this land still bears in the Everglades and the coasts are so much older than the region itself that thought grows dizzy contemplating them.

Eight hundred million years ago there were growing on the warm lands then far north palmlike plants called cycads. They grow on the borders of the Everglades now. The ants were already fixed in their selfless habits of busyness, as they are today. The first reptiles, shaped like the small green lizards on the sun-warmed stones, had taken to the air and learned to fly, having changed their scales to wings, one hundred and fifty-five million years before there was any Florida at all.

The little scorpions that crawl out of rotted wood on cold nights and hang on a wall like perfect small lobsters, whose species have the longest history of any air-breathing thing, are older than any of this rock of which the Floridian world is made. The sponges, the corals, the shellfish, some of the crabs along these coasts, the tiniest shell forms that turn up in the muck below the oldest saw grass, are older than the whole shape of this land. There are forms among these hammocks more ancient by a hundred million years. The most recent dragonfly that crawls from its larval state to dry and stretch its glistening fine wings on the tallest saw grass was shaped and formed so many centuries before the whole contour of the Everglades began that one looks from the insect to the wideness of this grassy world with a feeling that understanding of permanence is, like an understanding of time itself, impossible.

Only yesterday, then, they say, the Floridian plateau was lifted up, long after the quails and the swifts and the flamingos, the warblers and the water snakes, the owls, the woodpeckers and the alligators had assumed their present forms and habits.

The north of Florida may have been a part of the north mainland before the West Indian islands rose in the fire of their own volcanoes from the edge of a huge fault in the ocean bottom that skirts the inmost deeps. The questing shadows of sharks ranged freely throughout all the oceans, east to west, before Central America was an isthmus. There were monkeys in the world and gibbons and that brooding incalculable new thing in the other continent, this shambling figure with the spark under his thick skull that was the beginning of all thought —man. The Everglades were not begun before him.

But in that farthest age of the recent they call the Miocene, when the shape of the Florida plateau was forced up out of the sea, it was the last such rising movement, or so most of the scientists think, that occurred here.

There are no loopings and foldings of this rock, no tilted broken strata here. There is only, far below the surface, the evidence of that old, old first movement, a slow, smooth, regularly marked ancient dome. The top of the dome, the anticline, is highest north of Okeechobee, near the center of north Florida at Ocala. From Ocala southward, like the slopes of a deep-hidden hill, the strata flow downward, farther and farther below. The oldest, the Cretaceous, which first existed one hundred twenty million years ago, is the lowest, sweeping down ten thousand feet below the southern rim of the Everglades and of the sea. The Eocene lies above that and the Oligocene above that, and the Miocene curves from north to south under Okeechobee and the Everglades from ninety to nine hundred feet below the surface. The surface itself, this oölitic limestone, lies from the surface to ninety feet down under the southern mangrove rim.

All those strata, from the dome at Ocala, sweep down and farther down in regular flowing layers. So that what is on the surface in north Florida, the water-bearing rock that makes the lovely north Florida springs and cavernous rivers "measureless to man," is hidden under the Everglades by a thousand feet. From that rock nothing reaches up to the surface here. That is why only the surface rain water that flows into Okeechobee makes the Everglades and seeps into and frets the rock. There are no upgushings from deep subterranean rivers.

It proves again that, since the Miocene, those nineteen million years ago, there has been no change in the larger shape of the Floridian plateau itself. What happened, to surface that hidden dome with limestone and sand and marl and muck and peat, was the phenomenon of the polar ice.

Ice that had formed at the poles, in a world then tropic almost to what we now call the Arctic Circle, in an age of warmth began to move slowly downward in enormous encroaching glaciers, huge mile-high cliffs of ice that scraped and tore and gouged away rocks and mountains in their courses and sucked up water from all the oceans as they froze, in a slowly chilling world. Perhaps the mountains had been thrust up too high, so that too much snow had fallen. Perhaps there was less sunlight, from the tornadoes of shadow that pass across the surface of the sun itself.

At least, the scientists are sure of the ice. It moved southward, in the Northern Hemisphere, killing the forests, shoving the changing forms of living things all southward, scarring and grinding the face of the world. It never reached Florida.

Then, after an interminable cold and shadowy time, the warmth came back. The glacial polar ice melted and retreated, and all that released water flowed back into the seas. The sea rose up over the edges of that new shape of the Floridian plateau, warming and washing it gently, moving north of Okeechobee in a long curve over the once-risen land.

Four times in that measureless age of ice the glaciers froze and formed again and crept grating and jarring southward, in the fogs and glacial mists, beyond the Great Lakes and New York State and New England. Again freezing, they drew up the waters of the earthly seas. When they melted and left the deep gouged lakes and the ice-worn rounded hills and the glacial moraines, they gave back the waters to the sea again. But in some places there had been faultings and enlargings in the ocean's undersurface, and huge lakes were left filled with water so that each time the sea rose back over lower

Florida it never reached its earlier levels. Each time the curving waterline was lower.

Okeechobee was left then as a great inland fresh-water lake, a swampy amorphous depression. From this, the powerful rains leached away the salt. On the east coast the lines of retaining ridges were left as they may be seen today, all parallel, north and south but each lower, as between the glacial stages the sea each time did not stand so high.

The slow retreating waves dropped their silt between the great glacial periods. Below the waterline there was water erosion, holes in the shoreward rocks smooth scoured by the sand and the tides. The marl at the south accumulated softly. The fresh-water limestone was established. By the lines of shell fossils geologists can today trace the old sea levels. A last glacier took up the water and the sea shrank back and the fresh water from Okeechobee flowed out and down the slow incline. The western rivers swept farther out along the soft rock than they do now, dropping the scoured silt and sand in outer peninsulas and bars and wind-swept dunes for the sea to shape.

Then that last glacier melted and retreated farther north than it ever had before. It is there now, the north polar icecap, the glaciers, the ice fields of the arctic, the thick ice over Greenland and inner Alaska and northern Siberia. Not all the water was returned to the sea. But there was enough to change again the changing shape of lower Florida. The sea crept back up the mouths of the western rivers, filling and submerging the outer shape of Caloosahatchee, creeping up toward the Everglades in all those shapeless, spreading, wandering tidal rivers among the mangroves, filling up the sand dunes so that they became the Ten Thousand Islands.

On the east coast, along that highest rim of rock, the south-swinging current that edges between the Gulf Stream and the land laid down sand in bars and peninsulas, filled up some of the mouths of rivers like the Loxahatchee, and laid the sand again along the ridgy shapes of the keys. On the south the sea crept over the marly shallows and kept the currents between the keys open, and they filled the Bay of Florida, and laid down the sand of Cape Sable and worked the standing salt ponds and lagoons of the Everglades delta shore.

The sea had risen. It is there now. The shape of this land was established. The long flow of time seems to have slowed to its humdrum working of day to day. Yet if this is the end of the ice age, or if the sea is still rising and the ice melting, if there will be other ages of ice and sunlessness when the seas are taken up and the moist hidden caverns of the lower deeps again revealed, who can guess? Time never stops.

So down the valley of the Glades the fresh water crept in its recent shape, recent by centuries unrecorded except for the rock. The saw grass, one of the oldest forms of green life on the already aged earth, thrust up here its first sharp, resilient spears.

After it, in the earth now seeming so long established, the forms old and new of plant and animal and insect life hurried to take their hold.

Time moves again for the Everglades, not in ages and in centuries, but as man knows it, in hours and days, the small ʼents of his own lifetime, who was among the last of the ʼg forms to invade its shores.

VI. LIFE ON THE ROCK

THE saw grass and the water made the Everglades both simple and unique. Life, fighting for bordering and encroaching on that simplicity, life lives upon on its coasts and islands, a diversity of ʼk that holds it. The saw grass in its es-

sential harshness supports little else. It repelled man. But on the rock the crowding forms made life abundant, so that between the two the chronicle is balanced.

One begins with the plants.

If the saw grass here is four thousand years old, many other of these plant associations may have been here almost as long.

In the time of which I write, toward the end of the past century when everything was as it had been, the southern vague watery rim of Okeechobee was bordered by a strange jungle. The crusted wave foam was washed down among windrows of dead reeds and branches and rotting fish. In that decay a wide band of jungle trees sprang up.

Southwest it was all custard apple, a subtropic, rough-barked, inconspicuous tree, with small pointed leaves and soft fruits. It grew fiercely, crowded on roots that became gnarled trunks or trunks twisted and arched into bracing roots in the drag of the water. The spilth and decay of the custard apple, the guano of crowds of birds that fed on them, whitening the leaves, built up in the watery sunlessness below them an area of rich black peat, denser than muck, two or three miles wide and six or eight feet deep.

The earliest Americans on the lake called this area "the custard apple bottoms." It was edged with tall leather ferns and Boston ferns and knotted with vines, which no man could get through without axes or dynamite. Lake water crept darkly below.

The southeast was edged with a less tropical jungle, scrub willow with its light-green pointed leaves and yellow catkins and the ropy brown bark of elderberries, bearing out of their lacy plates of white blossoms the purple-black fruit about which the blue jays and the mockingbirds, the great black-glinting Florida crows, the grackles and the red-winged blackbirds in their thousands set up a flapping and creaking and

...ees and bright flies and yellow but-
crowing and ker-e-ne blossoms were sweet. Under their
terflies hovered ...ers moved sluggishly. Winds carried to
shadows groundy lake clouds of feeble white insects lake
them from t[z]le winks," which breed and die in myriads in
people callys.

a short f...re the willow-and-elder bottoms, which fought
The... with the saw grass for every rocky space. The dark-
shre... peaty muck they left went east up the lake edge between
br... sand ridges and the saw-grass arms.

Over all this thick jungle region climbed and hung down
in moving green curtains the heart-shaped leaves of moon-
vines. In the luminous unseen dark of the night the moonflowers opened acres after acres of flat white blossoms, cloud
white, foam white, and still. Northward, lake water moved
darkly under the tiny pointed reflections of the stars. Below
the region the moonflowers and the moon made their own,
with no man's eye to see them, moved the enormous darkness
without light of the saw-grass river.

East along the curving Everglades borders and west by the
farther coast stood everywhere in their endless ranks the great
companies of the pines. Where they grew the rock was highest—"high pine land," people called it. Their ranks went off
across an open slough in a feathery cliff, a rampart of trunks
red-brown in the setting sun, bearing tops like a long streamer
of green smoke. Their warm piny breaths blew in the sun
along the salt winds. They covered here, as they did everywhere in Florida, interminable miles.

Some southern longleaf, "common yellow pine," with its
taller trunk and bushier branches is scattered south from the
Caloosahatchee and down the east coast to the New River. But
below there, wherever it could find foothold in high rock, and
up behind the western mangrove to what is now Gordon Pass,

which is the area of West Indian vegetation, grows the Caribbean pine. It stands everywhere about the borders of the
Caribbean. It is called slash pine. But in Dade County from the
first it was called Dade County pine.

Its trunks are set thick with rust and brown and grayish bark
patches, which resist fire. The patterns of its skimpy branches
people find strange, or beautiful. Dying alone, as they often do
away from their great companies, killed by lightning or the
borer that instantly finds injured bark, these pines stand dead
a long time, rigid gray or silver, their gestures frozen. The
young fluffy pines start up everywhere about them, bearing
long pale candles in the new light of spring.

With the Caribbean pines, as they do with other pines of
the South, always grow the palmettos. These are saw palmettos,
silver-green, blue-green, or in dry times magnificent tawny-
gold across vast open savannas. Their spiky fans cover all the
ground beneath the pine trees, on unseen spiny trunks. If they
are burned, with a great oily popping and seething, only the
blackened trunks are left, writhing like heavy snakes.

The small brown Florida deer step neatly at the edge of pine
forests like these. The brown wildcats know them. The clear
light falls mottled through the branches faintly green over endless fan points. Inconspicuous wild flowers grow in the wiry
grass between palmettos, faint blue chicory, or yellow tea bush,
or the tiny wild poinsettias with their small brush strokes of
scarlet. The quail pipe and their new-hatched young run like
mice with their small cheeping, at the edge of such pineland,
and the brown marsh rabbit with small ears and no apparent
tail nibbles some bit of leaf.

A diamondback rattlesnake may push out here slowly after
such a rabbit or the cotton mice, or lie after shedding his flaky
old skin to sun the brilliant dark lozenge marks on his almost
yellowish new scales, slow to coil or rattle unless angered. Then

in a blur he draws back in quick angles that wide-jawed head with the high nose balanced over the coils, his slitted eyes fixed and following his object, the forked tongue flicking through the closed jaws, tasting the disturbed air. His raised tail shakes the dry rattle of its horny bells. His strength, his anger, engorges that thick muscular body, ruffles his barky scales. If he strikes it is at one-third of his length. The jaws open back so that the long fangs strike forward and deep. His recovery is quicker than the eye can see. Or he lifts tall that kingly head before he lowers it in retreat, holding himself grandly, with the same dignity that has made him the king among all these beasts.

All the woodpeckers in south Florida yank and hitch and cluck and rap their way up these great patched pine trunks, all with red heads, the downy, the hairy, the red-bellied, and that diabolical creature with a red and white and black head like a medieval battle-ax, the pileated, which the early settlers called so truly "the Lord God Almighty." But in those early days the even more impressive ivory-billed, which we shall never see again, startled these pinewoods with his masterly riveting.

Even in the middle of the saw-grass river, where an outcrop of old rock is the only evidence of preglacial times, the pines grow tall to show where the rock lies. The buzzards and the black vultures, their ragged wing tips like brush strokes of India ink, sail and sail and rise on the upcurrents and soar in their pure flight, turning about some old roost they have always kept and returned to year after year. Their piercing glances watch for the glint of flies' wings over carrion they crave, the most valuable birds in the world. Or from the muddy water holes about the pineland the brown-black water moccasins slide their wet ridged scales. Startled, they coil to retract those open, white-lined jaws, like a queer white flower to anything peering down. Death is there too.

Where the pines are thin, the Indians found their first source of life. There grow foot-tall, ferny green cycads, plants older than this rock, with yellow and orange cones for flowers and great thick roots. This is the "coontie" of the oldest Indian legend. Its root is grated and squeezed and sifted to flour to make the thick watery gruel "sofkee," which was always the basis of the Indians' diet here. The Indians' legend came partly from the Spanish fathers. They say that once there was a great famine here in Florida. The Indians prayed to the Master of Breath, who sent down His Son, God's Little Boy, to walk about at the edge of the pinelands and the Glades. And wherever He walked, there in His heel marks grew the coontie, for the Indians to eat and reverence.

Sometimes it is called compte. The early white men learned of it and grated it to make starch and knew it as arrowroot. By the pinelands north of the Miami River, the Indians camped often, so that their women could gather it in what was called the Coontie grounds.

The dragonflies on iridescent wings dart and hang in squadrons by the open air of pinelands. Below among the grass roots stirs all the minute dustlike activity of the ants.

In the summer hosts of big red-and-yellow grasshoppers, with heads shaped like horses', will descend and eat holes in all the softer leaves. Walking sticks fly like boomerangs. Shining brown leaf-shaped palmetto bugs scurry like cockroaches. Spiders like tiny crabs hang in stout webs. The birds snap at small moths and butterflies of every kind. A blue racer, the snake that moves across the cleared sand like a whiplash, will with one flick destroy the smooth, careful cup of the ant lion in the hot sand. The whole world of the pines and of the rocks hums and glistens and stings with life.

But if, on these rocky outcrops, the pines and the palmettos were destroyed, by lightning or the old fires of Indians, another great tree took its place and gradually changed, with its own associated forms, the whole nature of the place. This was the live oak, the first of the hardwoods. They made the first hammocks at the edge of rivers or on the driest Everglades islands.

The warblers in their thousands migrate up and down the continents, spring and fall, South America to North America and back, enlivening the oaks with their small flitting shapes and tiny whisperings; palm and pine warblers, the myrtles, the black-throated blues, the amazing redstarts, the black-and-whites—oh, it is impossible to name all the warblers that pass here.

Dozens of other birds are there in their seasons in the live oaks, among the red splashes of air plants and the patches of lichens. Green lizards puff out their throats like thin red bubbles in some unhearable love call. The eternal cardinals raise their first trillings before dawn, "Pretty, pretty, pretty—sweet, sweet-sweet." A mocking bird, all one whirl of gray and white, flips through those aging branches chasing a small brown owl or flinging him in the sun from the topmost twigs to fling up his modulated lovely spray of words. The small tree-frogs pipe there in the gray before rain and the yellow-billed cuckoo croaks, and the almost invisible rain-crow. In the first tender dark the little owl comes out from his hole where the mocker chased him to begin his low, liquid bubbling, the velvet secret voice of the night.

South in the lower hammocks in a live oak, frowsy with dry Resurrection ferns that the first rain startles to green life, some pale green slender stalk with minute gold eyes will seem to grow along a branch, poking upward on its own thoroughfare, high and higher in the leafiness, a small green tree snake. Such little snakes achieve the sun among the topmost leaves to be spied on by one of the loveliest bird-shapes of all, the free-fly-ing, easy-soaring, easy-turning swallow-tailed kite, that lifts and ranges and swings in whiteness above the tree-tops. One stoop and the free bird slides upward on the wind, dangling the small tender green thing in pure sunlight to its airy and exalted death.

A huge ancient line of live oaks stands along the westernmost rock edge of Okeechobee, deep with moss, looking out over miles and miles of shallow reeds between them and the mirage-like glitter of that inland sea. There in open, sunblasted country the black-and-white caracara, that the Mexicans take for their national eagle, cries harshly from a bush top, his round, gold glance avid for lizards on the ground. A king snake, brave in yellow and fine black in the dust, snaps back in zigzags the speed of his fighting body. Grackles in thousands, creaking their interminable wheels of sound, hang in the reeds their thousands of pouchlike nests. Life is everywhere here too, infinite and divisible.

The live oaks, like dim giants crowded and choked by a thrusting forest of younger hardwoods, made that great Miami hammock, the largest tropical jungle on the North American mainland, which spread south of the Miami River like a dark cloud along that crumbling, spring-fed ledge of rock. Here where the leaf-screened light falls only in moving spots and speckles to the rotting, leaf-choking mold, the hoary ruins of live oaks are clouded by vines and resurrection ferns, their roots deep in the rotting limestone shelves among wet potholes green-shadowed with the richest fern life in the world—maidenhair and Boston ferns and brackens and ferns innumerable. At night the mosquitoes shrill in the inky blackness prickled through with fireflies.

About the live oaks is waged the central drama of all this jungle, the silent, fighting, creeping struggle for sunlight of the strangler fig. It is one of those great trees people call rubber trees or Banyans. They are all *Ficus*, but the strangler is *Ficus aurea*. A strangler seed dropped by a bird in a cranny of oak bark will sprout and send down fine brown root hairs that dangle and lengthen until they touch the ground. There they grip and thicken and become buttresses. Over the small hard oak leaves the thick dark-green oily strangler's leaves lift and shut out the sun. Its long columnar trunks and octopus roots wrap as if they were melted and poured about the parent trunk, flowing upward and downward in wooden nets and baskets and flutings and enlacings, until later the strangler will stand like a cathedral about a fragment of tree it has killed, crowning leaves and vast branches supported by columns and vaultings and pilings of its bowery roots.

The stranglers are only the most evident and dramatic of all these crowding tropical jungle trees; smooth red-brown gumbo limbos, ilex, eugenias, satinwoods, mastic, cherry laurel, paradise trees, the poisonous manchineel, the poisonwood, the Florida boxwood and hundreds more which the hurricanes brought over from Cuba and the West Indies.

This was the jungle that people thought the Everglades resembled. Birds flit through it only rarely. The little striped skunk leaves its trail. The brilliant coral snake buries its deadly black nose in its loam. The false coral, the harlequin, with its yellow nose, is hardly less hidden. Spiders stretch their exquisite traps for pale insects. Small brown scorpions move on the rotting logs. And far up among the tufted air plants the small native orchids are as brown and pale yellow and faint white as the light they seek.

Everywhere among these branches moves imperceptibly one of the loveliest life forms of these coasts—the pale-ivory, pale-coral, pale-yellow and pale-rose, whorled and etched and banded shell of the *Liguus*, the tree snails. Their pointed shell bubbles are found chiefly on smooth-barked trees in the dry

hammocks, but every Everglades island-hammock has its own varieties, subspecies developed in countless lifetimes in a single unique area, varying with an infinity of delicate differences. They came from the tropics. They are a world in themselves.

Moths move in and out of the light at the jungle edge, the twilight hawk moth, seeking the pale-flowered vines, and the rose-colored tiger moth. There is a day in the spring when myriads of white butterflies drift over the whole land, moving out to sea inexplicably. They are caught and die in thousands against the jungles.

But here especially the strangest of the butterflies quivers silently in the bands of sun in the green light of leaves, the only one of its tropical kind on this mainland. It is the *Heliconius*, named for the sun, barred black and pale yellow as the light and shade, wavering always in companies, which no bird will touch. The *Heliconius* drowse of nights in colonies, delicately crowded and hanging on a single small tree. When bright moon light reaches them they have been seen to wake and drift about, filling a leafy glade with their quivering moon-colored half-sleep.

About the rivers of the west, north of the tropic vegetation line, grows the water oak. The water oaks grow taller and more regular than the live oaks. Their longer pointed leaves drop off the bare boughs in a brief winter and put on their new light green long before the rusty live oaks renew themselves, in that misty river country. Both crowd down to the glossy water and make landscapes like old dim pictures where the deer came down delicately and the cows stand, to drink among their own reflections.

In the great Miami hammock, along the banks of almost every river, bordering the salt marshes, scattered in the thinner pineland, making their own shapely and recognizable island-hammocks within the Everglades river, everywhere, actually, except in the densest growth of the saw grass itself, stands the

Sabal palmetto. To distinguish it from the low shrubby saw palmetto, it is called the cabbage palm. With its gray-green fans glittering like metal in the brilliance, its round top bearing also branches of queer blossoms and hard dark berries, the cabbage palm grows singly or in dramatic clumps over stout round trunks. The basketwork of old fan hilts is broken off below as the trunk grows tall and smooth. Ferns and vines and air plants and lizards and spiders live in that basketwork. They are often engulfed by strangler figs. They bristle on the banks of fresh-water rivers among the oaks. They make dense islands in the saw-grass river.

They are a northern growth, unrelated to the tropical palms, to the coconut palms that rise above the outer beaches and are set everywhere in cities, or the great royal palms that tower among the Everglades keys and in a few magnificent hammocks of their own toward the west coast. The Spaniards introduced the coconuts to Panama from the Philippines, the royals are native West Indians. Their nuts were blown over from Cuba and germinated in the rain-washed debris of some tropical cyclone. Other delicate palms, like the silver palm of the lower mainland, came the same way.

Then there is the enduring cypress. There are many cypresses in the world but the Everglades region has two: the short, often dwarf, pond cypress and the tall fresh-water river cypress. It is the river cypress that is tall, to 125 feet, silver gray, columnar, almost pyramidal on its broad fluted base, whose curiously short branches lose their leaves in winter and stand ghostly and gaunt among the hanging Spanish moss and red-tongued air plants. Spring draws out from the ancient wood the tiny scratched lines of its thready leaves, the palest yellow-green darkening to emerald. It is a fine timber tree. White and green, over brown water, against an amazing blue and white sky, it is most strangely beautiful.

The cypress that grows in muddy water has that curious accompaniment, the rootlike extension into the air, like dead stumps, called cypress knees, which are thought to aerate the mudbound roots. The dry-land cypress does not need them. It grows up rivers of both coasts and about the lake. But in its greatest area, a vast dramatic association of river cypress and pond cypress marks the west bank of the saw-grass river, and forms the Big Cypress Swamp.

The Big Cypress extends south from the Devil's Garden, a wilderness of pine and scrubby stuff and bushes, near that dome of land in the angle of Caloosahatchee and the lake, south in great fingers which reach to the headwaters of the Turner River, as far down as the salt water and the mangrove. The rock below it is uneven and ridgy, all hollows and higher places. It is called "swamp" because in the rains the water stands in it and does not run off. It is not moving water, like the saw-grass Glades. It was called "the Big Cypress" because it covered so great an area.

The river cypresses stand there in wintertime in great gray-scratched heads, like small hills, towering above the dense and lower pond, or dwarf, cypress between, thinly set in the wetter hollows of wire grass, starred with white spider lilies and sedges and, in drier places, milkwort in saffron-headed swaths. Red-shouldered hawks cruise the low cypress and the marshlands, marsh hawks balance and tip, showing white rump marks, and far over at the edge of a thicket a deer feeds, and flicks his white-edged tail before he lifts his head and stares.

From high in a plane at that time of year the Big Cypress seems an undulating misted surface full of peaks and gray valleys changing to feathering green. East of it, sharply defined as a river from its banks, move the vast reaches of the saw grass.

The brown deer, the pale-colored lithe beautiful panthers that feed on them, the tuft-eared wildcats with their high-angled hind legs, the opossum and the rats and the rabbits have lived in and around it and the Devil's Garden and the higher pinelands to the west since this world began. The quail pipe and call through the open spaces. The great barred owls hoot far off in the nights and the chuck-will's-widows on the edge of the pines aspirate their long whistling echoing cries. The bronze turkeys, the most intelligent of all the birds or beasts, feed in the watery places and roost early in the thick cypress tops, far from the prowlers below. And the black Florida bear, which sleeps even here his short winter sleep, goes rooting and grumbling and shoving through the underbrush, ripping up logs for grubs and tearing at berries, scorning no mice.

The bears move to the beaches and, like the panthers, dig for turtle eggs. They catch crabs and chew them solemnly and eat birds' eggs if they find them, and ripe beach plums. The panthers prey most on the range hogs of the settlers, and so they are hunted with dogs, and fight viciously, killing many before they leap into trees and, snarling, never to be tamed, are shot.

Here in the cypress pools—but for that matter, everywhere in the watery Glades, from lake to sea—lives the Glades' first citizen, the otter. Like the birds, he is everywhere. The oily fur of his long lithe body is ready for heat or cold, so long as it is wet. His webbed hands are more cunning than the raccoon's. His broad jolly muzzle explores everything, tests everything, knows everything. His quickness is a snake's lightning quickness. He has a snake's suppleness and recovery, but not the snake's timidity. His heart is stout and nothing stops him.

The otter has been seen to swim and flirt and turn among a crowd of thrashing alligators, from whose clumsy attack he has only to dive and flash away. He knows how to enjoy life in the sun better than all the rest of all the creatures. He is gay. He is crammed with lively spirit. He makes a mud slide down a bank, and teaches his cubs to fling themselves down it and romp and tumble and swim upside down in the frothing water. He is fond of his female and plays with a ball and has fun. His ready grinning curiosity and friendliness betray him to the hunter and trapper. This is his home.

On the scanty dwarf cypress the gray Ward's heron stands rigid. The big black-and-white wood ibis, like a stork, which flies so high and so far in such grave and orderly squadrons, slides downward on hollow wing and lights with a great flapping and balancing that makes the tree look silly under its teetering grip as it stares down its great curved beak for a frog there below. It is as though all the life of the Everglades region, every form of beast or bird or gnat or garfish in the pools, or the invisible life that pulses in the scum on the pools, was concentrated in the Big Cypress.

The dwarf cypress has its area, perhaps the most fantastic of all, far toward Cape Sable, south of the live-oak jungle that was called Paradise Key, where the royal palms stood high overhead like bursting beacons seen across the sloughs. Men have said they have seen panthers here, not tan, but inky black. There southward, under the even more brilliant light, as if already the clouds reflected the glare from the sea beyond, the small cypress, four or five feet tall, stands in the rock itself, barely etched with green. These trees seem centuries old, and they are very old indeed, in spite of fire and hurricane. Even in full leaf their green is scant. There are moccasins around their roots out of the standing clear water, and high, high over, a bald eagle lazily lifting, or an osprey beating up from the fishing flats.

Lake jungles, pine, live oak, cabbage palmetto, cypress, each has its region and its associated life. As the islands in the saw grass pointed southward in the water currents, their vegetation changes like their banks, from temperate to subtropic, to the full crammed tropic of the south.

The northernmost are dense with pond apple or willow and elder and those charming border shrubs, the silver myrtle, with its spring flowering of silky silvery pompons, the day jasmine, with the dark berries the mocking birds clamor for, salt bush, bay, and dozens of others. There are hammocks centered about live oaks or cabbage palms, crowded and screened with bushes. There are cypress hammocks hung with moss over a deep brown pool where a single heron waits and the blue flag and the water hyacinth and the green arrowy lilies catch a great shaft of light. Beyond lies all that broad, open, windy level of the Glades.

So, at the end of the saw-grass river and its bordering coasts, begins the mangrove. It shows itself in short tufts first, in green leggy rosettes far south where the saw grass is shorter over thinner muck and the emerging rock. There are higher hammocks of mangrove beyond. The saw-grass river goes on around them. In the rainy seasons the current is visible, rippling and bending the grass tops as it flows nearer the sea. The draining fresh-water rivers begin far above the highest salt tides.

Glaring under the sun or bleak in the rain, flat, with patches of scrub and bright salt weeds, this is the country of the birds. The man-o'-war birds from the keys float and tumble over it in their effortless flight. Thousands of sandpipers and sanderlings rise in clouds from the water meadows. The ducks paddle in every stream end. In some great inland bay of salt water, two or three hundred white pelicans, like a snowbank on a reef, wait for the tide to drive the small fish into their scooping beak-pouches. They are ten feet from wing tip to wing tip. When they rise, fraying out, peeling off, in a slow roar of aroused wings, they float high up and sail and turn in great concentric circles, white against cloud dazzle.

The headwaters of these fresh-water rivers are covered in the season with the stick nests of herons, the least blue and the glossy and the Louisiana and the solitary great white heron, the stalker of these shallows. The roseate spoonbills, with their queer bills and delicate, flame-stained pink feathers, have gone through their ridiculous stick courtships here. And drifting down from the saw-grass reaches come the white ibis, in a huge sweeping, turning, flashing circle, tilted groundward so that the lower birds stop and stand with outstretched necks before they are caught up again in the wheeling flying, the rare pattern of their nuptial flight.

Like the otter, raccoons are everywhere about the Everglades, but here in the south by the mangrove they have lived in thousands. Their wonderful small black fingers find the crawfish and the sea grape and the coon oysters hanging on the mangrove roots. They stand on their hindquarters with their hands on their furry chests to snuff at every wind with those sharp curious noses, peering at everything strange with those black-masked bright eyes.

Within the salt meadows here at the end of this world, green with thick-stemmed waterweeds glowing yellow and coral about the white marly water, the round-nosed dark alligators find their way along fresh-water inland streams, after their fierce matings, to make their nests.

There must be heat and wetness for the porous thirty or more eggs the female alligator lays. She works together a great mass of waterweeds or grass, mashing it down and letting it rot and grow compact, and brings new stuff in her toothy jaws to pile on it. When it is settled and steaming she pushes the top off and makes a hole and lays her eggs and covers them again. It may take eight weeks or more, with the sun heat and the ferment and the moisture, to incubate them.

When the young squeak in their shells she comes back and pushes the stuff from off their lively tails and bright eyes and tiny jaws, ready, direct from the shell, to snap at minnows.

But the crocodile, the narrow-jawed, clay-colored faster beast, goes no farther inland than the warm beaches to dig a hole in dry sand and lay dozens of eggs that any moisture may destroy. Their clay-colored slitted eyes watch unblinking among the mangrove-stained watercourses, vicious, intractable, and vanishing. This last is their country.

So, fringing the salt marshes or the higher saw-grass meadows of the southeast, where the deer make their paths, there begins in earnest the dark mangrove wilderness. It is a world as monotonous, as unique, as the saw grass. It looks as if there was nothing here but mangroves and the mud stinking with vegetable rot and saltreek and the moving sea water.

Mangroves exist in many places in the tropics. But this area is the most magnificent mangrove forest, and the greatest, in the American hemisphere.

Two kinds of mangroves dominate this association, the black and the red. It begins on the last peat with tall hammocks and forests of buttonwoods, called "white mangrove," not a true mangrove at all but *Conocarpus*. Then in the first level of the high tide stands deep-rooted the black mangrove, the *Avicennia nitida*, not tall, but thick, which often sends from its submerged roots up through two or three feet of mud and water the curious pneumatophores, like thousands of sharp bristling sticks, most difficult to wade through. They are breathing organs. The dark-green leaves above them often exude salt crystals. The roots stain the water brown with strong tannin.

Beyond that, marching out into the tides low or high, and rooted deep below them in marl over the rock, goes the great *Rhizophora*, the red mangrove, on its thousands of acres of entwined, buttressed and bracing gray arches. The huge trunks, often seven feet in circumference, stand as high as eighty feet here, one hundred in the drier spots. Their canopy of green obliterates the sky. In the shadowy light over that world of arches over water all is clear gloom.

Entering wave ridges are beaten down, here. The foam washes in all the flotsam of the sea, the accumulated drift of the shallows. The thick leaves turn yellow continually and continually fall. The decay rises among those arches and the younger growths slowly march seaward across it, holding and building the land.

From the high branches long hairy ropes swing and hang down to reach the water and branch into roots. Some have few fruits. Some are heavy with long seeds like small thin torpedoes, which fall and stick in the mud under low tide and grow. But more commonly they float and are carried endlessly on sea currents that bring them upright and alive, ready to root, on other far mangroveless tropic shores.

Where these mangroves came from, to this young mud over the older rock, cannot be guessed. This may be one of the great parent forests from which seeds have been carried as far as the South Pacific. Nobody knows.

The mangrove here is at least as old as the Everglades, of which it marks the end.

The People of the Glades

Marjory Stoneman Douglas

THERE is no place on the American continents to which one can point and say, "Man began there."

To the white European who found man in the New World and promptly misnamed him "Indian" it was sufficient that he was here, where the Lord must have put him. It was centuries before white men began to realize that the Indian who had been here so long might have come from somewhere else. It is actually within the past few years that archaeological discoveries have added definite proof to that hypothesis.

To try, therefore, to explain how the Indian came to Florida by speaking of the southeastern states of the mainland, or even,

as some lingering believers in the Antillean theory like to do, of the Caribbean, is like accepting the Indians' belief that the white man sprang new and whole from the Atlantic Ocean.

We know that the human race did not originate on this side of the world at all, because in all North and South America there is not one trace of the evidence found abundantly in Europe-and-Asia, to show where man first stood up and became a man. A million years ago, they reckon, the piece of skull, two teeth and a thigh bone they found in Java was the first living shape of man about which they know anything. "Pithecanthropus erectus," man-first-standing-up, was not entirely a man yet, just as geologic Florida was not yet Florida. The time of that first man was the early Pleistocene, when the last upheaval began slowly lifting the Floridian shape upward through warm sea water. The glacial periods were still to come.

The history of man himself in this world is like the flow and spread and dividing of a great river. Man became the three races in that movement about the earth which must have taken place before all the land masses had ceased to shift, when the land bridges between Asia and North America, and at the isthmus between the Americas, were being joined and wrenched apart and joined again. The glaciers were still there. A million years ago man first appeared, and in that time, strange hostile parts of the same human whole, reached about the world.

The three races were men of three different colors, living in much the same way, urged by the same hungers. The pinky-tan one was to call himself "white," as he called the yellow-brown one "red" and "yellow," and the charcoal-and-coffee colored one "black."

One group of those Stone Age men moved from the Caucasus and held India and reached to the Atlantic and moved down into Africa. They were Caucasian. The black one, the Negroid, came later to Africa, and in some strange way Australia also, as if even after their beginning one land mass had been broken and shifted away from the other. The yellow-brown Mongolian looked east to the Pacific and crowded all that land from the Malay Peninsula to Siberia. They moved farther into the arctic cold, when they learned to wear animal skins and make and use fire. The descendants of some of those first Mongols would become Chinese, and much later, begin the long process of civilization while all Europe still lived in the Stone Age. As it was, to become Caucasian, Negroid, Mongoloid had taken five hundred thousand years.

They tramped and wandered in family groups, fearing and fighting all others like themselves, surviving the turmoils of glacial time by sheer developing intelligence. When the Mongoloids had reached the northeastern confines of Asia, and looked east still, they had come far, as men.

The beasts had gone that way before them.

Four million years before man, the age of the great mammals had begun. The greatest of the animals, the teeth of which have been found in Florida, began in that early time in Africa as a small river beast that wandered where rivers led, growing big ivory tusks and a nose slowly elongating and becoming flexible. Before the Andes had begun to wrinkle and be squeezed up in South America, this creature was prowling, urged forward not just by hunger, but by a love of wandering and by a curiosity stronger than in any other mammal except man himself. Millions of years later this first of the great beasts, with trunks and ivory tusks, the elephant-kind, had developed many forms. There were the mastodons, bigger than elephants, some with two pairs of upper and lower tusks, and the mammoths.

They were to push their way all over Europe and Asia and fill great areas of Siberia with their buried bones. In a time when a land bridge existed between Asia and Alaska the great-brained, lumbering, curious beasts had ventured over Bering Strait, into North America. Swaying and plodding forward, peering ahead with small wild eyes, they moved, generation after generation, down into the American continents. No other animal has ever walked so far, except man.

They went south from Alaska and plodded down the long land bridge into Central America, against a tide of animals developed down there and driven north by the antarctic ice. In North America also, as another ice age crowded down from the North Pole, mastodons and mammoths and species that had developed here alone, the Columbian mammoth and the huge imperial, standing fourteen feet high and carrying tusks curving down and up in huge ivory scythes, moved slowly before the cold into the warmth of Florida.

They stood switching their tails and trumpeting and trampling the mud of the early swamps and lakes and rivers of the Everglades region, tearing at vines from the jungle growth of trees, along what was to be the Caloosahatchee, where their teeth, like worn lumps of stone, have been found.

The little horses that, in the Siberian country, ran like rabbits on five toes, and that the flesh eaters found sweet, saved some of their lives by running two toes off. Long before the mammoths, they ran into North America by way of Alaska, or perhaps even by Europe, Iceland, and Greenland, to multiply into great herds on the American plains and develop into a horse called "Equus" which was nearly modern. They were all relatives of a horse called "Hippidion." Some of them went south into South America, before they were all extinct in North America. Some ran down into Florida and to the Everglades and were caught there and were never seen again.

North America had originated some species of its own, as did South America. Camels began here as little hopping creatures which developed larger bodies like deer, with long slender necks and long legs, which ranged in Florida in great herds.

There were in Florida two other deer besides the small native one we have now, along with a tiny deerlike creature called "Leptomeryx" and a giant pig like a wart hog, and some peccaries and a short-faced bear, a small rhinoceros from Africa and a heavier one, with no horns, came south from Alaska, an early bison with straight horns, now extinct, and a giant beaver, and many rats.

Up from South America, around by the Gulf Coast and into Florida, came tapirs and huge peccaries and two kinds of capybaras and a giant tortoise-armadillo seven feet long with flexible armor, and a great strange mammal called a glyptodont, with head and tail and feet sticking out of his heavy immovable shell.

These were the peaceful beasts, the leaf eaters. The flesh eaters followed them into Florida. There came an Asiatic lion, yellow as sunlight, and cougars and true wildcats, and a long-legged cat more than half lion. But the most spectacular of all was the saber-toothed tiger, perfectly named "Smilodon." He was a heavy-shouldered thing, named for his eight-inch long fangs that must indeed have given him an extraordinary grin. There was a small wild dog and a big early hyena with crushing jaws. Wolves ran in ferocious packs, dire wolves, larger than any wolf man has seen, howling across the open swamps to the bellowing of alligators and crocodiles, their slitted eyes gleaming back to the same moon.

The freezing northern airs kept the animals in the warm south and in that developing shape of Florida like a sack with no lower opening. Nowhere else in America was there to be a more crowded or richer or more varied animal life. The plains of Africa in modern times have held no more amazing collection of these beasts, solitary or running in herds, creeping, pushing, scampering, lumbering and chasing.

There would never be so great a variety again. Since the first

interglacial time no new genus of those vertebrate mammals has ever developed. Not one. After that, whole families, orders, genera, over half or even two-thirds of the animal-kind then existing have ceased to exist anywhere on this earth.

Why so many should have become extinct here, no one knows accurately. Perhaps it was because there were too many of them, too many grass eaters for the grass, too many flesh eaters for the flesh. Perhaps they were overwhelmed by the readvancing seas of interglacial meltings that brought the bones of whales to lie among the deep beds of fossil shells which the Caloosahatchee in its meanderings would reveal. Perhaps the clumsy great things like glyptodonts and giant sloths and mammoths, weighed down by those extraordinary tusks, were caught and sank in swamps where the harrying wolves had chased them. The food of such beasts as Smilodon the tiger with his eight-inch fangs must have been snatched away from him by all the smaller, quicker cats, or perhaps the teeth that had grown so long grew longer and left him, mangy and starving, unable to open his jaws wide enough to kill or even to eat. The soil of Florida in all sorts of places is striated with their bones. The St. Johns and the Alachua plains are rich with them, the Manatee River and the Peace River, and the Caloosahatchee, the overrun edges of the Everglades and the Miami River.

It is only recently that scientists have been able to admit that the one other single factor which may have completed the extinction of all these strangely assembled early creatures may have been man.

They used to say it was impossible for him to have appeared on this continent more than ten thousand years ago. That would have been far too late for the complex era of the prehistoric animals. But startling discoveries made recently at Folsom, New Mexico, and at the Sandia cave, and most recently of all, at Alaska, have pushed back our knowledge of man's life here to nearly twenty thousand years ago. It may have been archaic man himself, nicking a tough hide with flint-tipped spears he learned to throw with whizzing accuracy, with spear throwers the later Mexicans would call "atlatls," and trotting tirelessly after a trail of blood until the beast died of bloodletting, or herding them with fires that may have devastated the early forests and begun the plains, drove amazing numbers of these creatures over cliffs to their deaths.

It is perhaps too easy to imagine archaic man in Florida whirling flaming brands to frighten away old Smilodon himself, famished and slinking into the swamps beyond. But man, the most destructive of all creatures at the beginning of his long career, may have been to some extent the death of them.

It is not considered scientific to put any faith in the myths and dreams of present-day Indians, as proof. But it is strange that in many of the old tales handed down to Indians today, as the fathers and mothers tell stories to sleepy children, and so carry on that extraordinary verbal racial memory of the Indian people, something like those shapes of vanished prehistoric beasts are outlined. There are tales that describe and refer to tigers and lions and elephants. There is a series of myths that seem to be about mammoths. Strange creatures give names to Indian diseases, and crowd Indian dreams with the forms of ancient nightmares. They were described by tellers of dreams and tellers of tales, from the oldest times.

Perhaps it means nothing that they speak of creatures with great crossed tusks or low creeping shapes, shadowy and vast and dangerous. There are tribes to the west that have stories of great animals with four legs and another leg that moves from a shoulder. There is that curious tale of the southeastern Indians, a nightmare or a myth that is known now as not much more than a ribald story to be laughed at about a hunting fire, of an enormous creature that drags a penis that can be moved

as high as the treetops. But what else would those shapes be but the memories of mammoths or of elephants with trunks for which the Indians would have no other words than such as their gusty humor gave?

They dream and that is not evidence. But the fears that a race has known lie deep and lasting in the dregs of the mind. The stories of ancient peoples are the unwritten records of memories and thoughts too old to be described accurately. Old shapes of incredible danger are made into stories for men to laugh at, or familiar words by which children are eased of fear of the dark, and so in comfort put to sleep. So a stouthearted people might deal with horror they once outfaced.

But if the animals came and became extinct, as the Everglades took shape out of the receding waters, it is certain that no animal life could compare with the wealth of the fish life about the newer coasts.

East, in the pale-green inshore currents the hordes of fighting fishes ran, the sharks and the barracuda, the mackerel, the bonito, the wahoo, the kingfish and the amberjack, moving in from the deeps to spawn and feed in the shoals. They crowded the bays and rivers. The silver mullet jumped before them among hissing acres of minnows as the big fish drove and ravaged behind them. Overhead the crowded sea birds screamed and swooped and fed. But south in the Bay of Florida and west up the coast over the shoals of the sunken Florida plateau trooped millions of other fish in long processions: the striped mullet, the snook, the snapper and the pompano, moving north and so around the shape of the Gulf of Mexico. The bays and passes were thick with fingerlings of every kind and the laughing gulls and the terns and the constant pelicans and the heavy mergansers preyed on them.

The green turtles of the outer sea came plowing heavily ashore to lay their eggs, which the bears and the panthers dug up. Out of the slow western mangrove rivers the small tarpon moved in the spring and grew huge and traveled east and west, rolling and exploding upward from night-colored waters in unbelievable bursts of crystal and silver under the whiteness of the tide-swelling moon.

If the fish were dense past belief, so were the shellfish. To this day, from that hidden floor of the western undersea plateau, where the sponges grew, the tides heap the western beaches with windrows of shells, ivory and yellow and rose-tinted, and crimson and orange and cream and mother-of-pearl, billions of shells. Tiny horns and delicate boats, and turrets and scoops and twisted ribbons and small brittle paws and blunt stars and crescents, they are piled up perfect and uninjured every day from that vast shelly sea-meadow. East coast too, among the gardens of branching corals and sea fans and sponges and black urchins and delicate anemones, where bright ribbons of small angelfish and parrot fish and moonfish stream and slide through green watery twilights, the shell creatures are everywhere.

There is a long reef south from the high dunes of Caxambas on the Gulf coast, which from the earliest known time was covered with miles and miles of the great thick-shelled clam that is called quohaug in the north, from which the New England Indians made their wampum. They are good eating too. On the arched mangrove roots of the west coast, which the tides cover and uncover, the small tasty mangrove oysters grow in clusters. Fine oysters grow there in bars beyond the mouths of lower rivers that bring them their food and the fresh water they must have.

More important were to be the great families of the conchs. They have always grown and been scattered up on these coasts, thousand upon thousands of great creamy whorled shells, like basket hilts of swords under the fluted apex, tapering to a long

grooved shank around the central spine, the columella. They house a solid fish-creature, footed like a huge snail, through the aperture that reveals the shining pink or yellow porcelain lining of the lip. Their gaudy china-satin has always caught the eye of sailors in warm seas. The garden paths and mantel-pieces of New England coast towns have long been decorated with them. These were the wreathed horns of Tritons of classical antiquities, and they are still the shells that teach listening inland children the faraway roaring of the sea. There is no end to the supply of them out of that brimming sea treasury.

They are called horse conchs, and king conchs, and queen conchs, but the Latin names are clearer. Everywhere there is a *Busycon perversum*, a brownish-white left-twisted fulgur. There is a *Strombus gigas*, the one with the wide gaudy pink lip. There is *Fasciolaria gigantea*, the great horse conch, sometimes as long as twenty-four inches, one of the two largest known shells in the world, univalve, solid as stone.

One of the most important sources of food, especially inland about the saw-grass river and the island hammocks, were the turtles. There were several fresh-water turtles which crawled also on land, the box turtle and the snapping turtles. But most important of all were the land turtles, the tortoises which pushed everywhere in the dust and ate grass, and much later were curiously called "gophers," and lived in holes.

Here they all were then, or forms like them.

There was man in Asia, crowded into the northeast limits, staring out in some time of the last ice age, wondering where it was out there that the food animals went.

He may have followed across ice the dripping blood trail of a mammoth he had wounded, and so struggled to another land, utterly unaware of the great step he took. Perhaps there were two or three hunters in a skin boat, who dared rough and gusty waters because behind them there was hunger. Not one of them was timid or satisfied to stay in crowded places. They were the boldest, the strongest, the most self-reliant of their kind. Of all those yellow-brown Mongolians they left, they were the most fit to be the first Americans. They were among the first of modern men.

They went east, and others followed them, in a long wavelike migration of people in small mobile groups, brown-faced people, with broad facial arches and straight black Mongolian hair. Their black eyes bore the Mongolian folds. Knowing nothing of what lay ahead, they pushed forward.

It is now thought that they must have penetrated the continent from some coastal bay like Kotzebue Sound and so into the valley of the Mackenzie and south to the broad plains and lakes of Saskatchewan, which lead south into the American plains. There they lived for more centuries than man knows, burning off the forests to drive the beasts and so increasing the plains area, developing some of that enormous variety of language groups known throughout the American hemisphere.

They were the archaic people, river dwellers, when they began to be known again, who came into northeastern Florida and lived along the St. Johns. That may have been even before the last of the interglacial water had been drawn off the south peninsula and the Everglades begun, into which they may have driven the last of the great prehistoric beasts. Their descendants lived there when the New World was discovered, calling themselves by a name which sounded to the Spaniards like "Timucua."

Centuries later, from somewhere west of the Mississippi, a movement was begun of people who spoke one of the languages of the greater speech group called "Muskogean." Some tribes of these made a slow way east along the Gulf of Mexico and the coastal strip of west Florida, and so down to the western shore of the Everglades and the tropic sea.

They were not archaic people, as the early Timucuans had been. They were the forerunners of the Indians of lower Florida. Long after they were established here, the Archaic Timucuans expanded westward all the way across the upper Florida peninsula, cutting off completely the strip down which the modern people had come. For hundreds of years the Glades people were cut off from further migration and developed slowly their own unique civilization.

They settled in three obvious main regions about the Everglades. The first, naturally, was the western, from north of the Caloosahatchee down through the Ten Thousand Islands to Cape Sable. Their name sounded to the later Spaniards something like "Carlos" or "Calos," which may have been derived from the Muskogee word "kalo," "black" or "powerful," and "ansha," "man" as far as is known. So that they were called the "Calusa" from the earliest people to late historic times. The people who moved to the great central lake that they called "Mayaimi," from the Muskogee "miaha," "wide," were called the "Mayaimi." Their neighbors in the same culture group who went to the east coast beaches were the "Jeaga" and those whom the Spaniards called "St. Lucie's." The Indians from Boca Raton south to Biscayne Bay and down the keys, are called by the word the Spaniards gave them, who thought they said something like "Tekesta."

We have no other names for them. In their three related divisions, they were the people of the Glades.

Because of the sun, the semitropical nature of the country about the saw grass, they made an immediate change in all their habits of living, like the intelligent people they were. They were to develop a culture completely their own.

The rough hot skin garments were discarded for cooler things in this country of the sun. The moss on the trees made excellent light skirts for the women, who did their work more freely with nothing above the waist. For breechclouts the men made a kind of plaited piece of palmetto strips, on a belt, and tied a bunch of moss on behind, not for decency, but to have something more comfortable to sit on than bare skin and bones. The young bucks presently changed the moss hanks to raccoon tails, very soft, very dashing.

It was a country without flints. It had no metals either, such as the people about Lake Superior had in these long centuries learned to mine and work. But here were the shells.

It must have been almost as soon as the first of the Glades people had come down to these beaches that a man wading in the warm clear shallows picked up one of those great left-handed conchs. The simplest way to get at the flesh would be to knock a hole in the side. But before he tossed the shell away empty, perhaps he balanced it thoughtfully in his hand. It was heavy as stone. If he could make another small hole in it he could take a stick of heavy mangrove wood and put it through the two holes, front and back, and lash it to that central spine at the right digging angle. If he ground the point and the lip sharply he would have a pick as good as any stone pick he ever used.

One of those smaller conch shells with the side cut off straight and the inside columella cut out would make as good a drinking cup as any gourd. A piece of one of those great shell lips ground sharp on one edge would make as good an ax as any stone. A hammer could be ground down from the heavy central column of the heaviest conch. Adzes for hollowing out logs for boats, chisels, net sinkers, heavy fishhooks, almost any kind of tool either men or women needed here could be picked up on those beaches. To grind a shell with sand and a piece of wood was slow work. But it was at least as easy as chipping flint.

They set their houses, mere open platforms on cabbage palm posts, roofed and thatched with the palmetto, in the sheltered water of inlets, at the mouths of rivers, and by streams from the lake and on the edges of the Glades. Some of the Calusa

houses were built on pilings out in the water or high on dunes in the winds. The roofs often covered two or three bedlike platforms between which they could walk and under which they could build smudge fires against the mosquitoes.

They gathered on dunes and sandbanks and beaches for great feasts of boiled and roast meat, because they were still flesh eaters, and some fish and oysters. They found sweet and tangy the cocoplums and beach plums and the wild grapes festooning the tall trees of the Caloosahatchee, and learned to eat the black massed berries of the palmettos. There were elderberries and sparkleberries and cabbage palm hearts to be cut. They did not at first bother with vegetables.

The brown, healthy, almost naked people, smeared with fish oils to keep off the mosquitoes or the sandflies, laughed and joked about the great cooking fires. Their careless hard heels trampled into the sand and ashes the bones, the discarded shells and all the leavings of their untidy roving lives. They came back again and again to the same feasting places. The piles they built up through centuries are called kitchen middens, refuse heaps which in time became accumulations of rich black dirt, with broken bits of their pottery and pieces of shells and bones. Some of these mounds are partly shell and partly black dirt, like the very early group of middens at Gordon's Pass, which marks the beginning of West Indian vegetation on the west coast, or at the headwaters, by the edge of the Big Cypress, of Turner's River.

In these easily worked first middens they also buried their dead. Human bones and teeth may be found there, two or three feet below the present surface, in the steaming, hard-packed and black lower earth.

It is believed certain now, although no one can be sure how long ago these people came into the Glades country, that they lived here somewhere around A.D. 900.

The pottery they made has told the story of their years more completely than anything else, to modern archaeologists. Pottery was for a long time the only expression of their real artistic ability. Their first pots were more like the sand-tempered ware of the Gulf region through which they had come, but they were smart enough to use local material with which to make their own. They shaped simple bowls by coiling over a flat base rolled ropes of soft clay, tempered with quartz sand, which John M. Goggin has named "Glades Plain," the earliest type of a long series called "Glades Gritty Ware." The pieces of such ware are still dark and heavy and gritty to the touch. No one bothered to decorate them.

When after many years the potters began to use decoration, the Calusas covered the whole rim with an over-all pattern of variously related, finely feathered lines. The Tekesta craftsmen about the Miami River, with hands growing firm and sure, dressed theirs with crosshatching, or bold repeated loops, or scallops cut with a swift thumbnail.

Then the east coast people used a new kind of paste to make the first of a series called "Biscayne Ware." It is called "chalky" because it has a smooth chalky surface which seems to rub off.

A third new ware, now called "Belle Glade," was developed by the Mayaimi Lake people. It was plain and very hard, marked only with the broad, unsmoothed strokes of a tool.

All such vessels, mouth down, were piled over with wood, and so crudely fired; red and brown and cream color and smoke-black.

Finally they stamped chalky ware pots, often colored with the red ocher they found in a place between what is now Fort Myers and Estero, with a paddle carved in a checked pattern, to be called "check stamped," which was carried far over the area and up the coasts.

It was about that time that they found hunting harder work

than fishing. It was easier to scoop up the fish that crowded the inlet-fishponds or herd them with a great yelling and shouting and thrashing of water and thumping of canoe sides, into the first fish weirs. They used three times as many net sinkers. They had more time too.

The last great period of the Glades culture began then, perhaps about A.D. 1200, when the developed skill of the craftsmen on the sound foundation of their ancient and individual culture blossomed in new freedom, an artistic renascence, of eager and elaborate experimentation. Everyone must have shared that expanding sense of new life.

It really began when someone invented a knife. He set sharks' teeth, the sharp, inch-long blades, into a wooden handle. It was a knife far superior for exact and delicate cutting to anything any Indian had ever used. The handles also were finely polished and carved at the upper end, with involved circles or rayed rosettes which might also have served as stamps. Other shark-tooth points were set at the side of carved handles the width of a palm, or two palms, for adzes. They made quantities of fine bone chisels and awls. They had rasps of sandstone and of sharkskin.

With the knives the craftsmen shaped something that delighted everybody: bone hairpins, three to ten inches long, with which to pin up their hot black hair. The pins were elaborately pretty, highly polished, carved with graceful designs, with carved wooden beads stuck on the ends inlaid cunningly with tortoise shell.

The Glades people from that time on had a lot of fun setting off their shapely brown bodies with all sorts of ornaments. They made pottery still, or perhaps the women did, but pots were dull things. The new art was not only an expression of their love of design, but what a man wore made him feel fine and attracted the girls.

They began to make and wear pendants, a unique Glades

fashion. They carved and perforated bones, deer bone and turtle bone and even human bone, perhaps the bones of a powerful enemy. They polished beautifully carved shell pendants to hang from their belts. They made large round shell ornaments to hang about their necks, and pierced also the occasional fresh-water pearls, or the curious vegetable pearls of the hammocks. They set wooden ear-plugs in shell rings, inlaid at the end with tortoise shell that looked like huge fish eyes. They bored holes in bits of pink and orange and mother-of-pearl shell lining, and bright red seeds, and shaped ivory columellas of conchs.

All those bright things clinked and winked and rattled and glittered on the oiled, shining copper bodies of those young hunters and warriors and fishermen, their black hair pinned up with pins and stuck with arrows. Their raccoon tails switched behind. The dark eyes of girls must have watched them from the house shadows as the self-conscious young men went by on the white sands, walking like dandies.

The social life around the seacoasts must have been a hearty and gay and colorful thing, among all those easy-muscled, graceful, assured people, bronze and dark in the whiteness of the light, with their great feasts and their songs that echoed from the canoes over the dark lagoons, and the laughter in moonlight, and the border wars that kept them tough. All these, the Calusas and the Mayaimis and the Tekestas, must have seemed to have been at home here forever.

Now after centuries, and before this time of the Glades renascence, the archaic river dwellers across the peninsula of Florida had become like the others to the north. Around Tampa the Spaniards later called them "Tocobago." Except in time of war, the canoes of the Calusas could now pass there in friendliness to northern trading places. They carried pottery and shell-work and bone pins, and their valuable pigment, red ocher, to barter for northern flints and galena and other pottery and some copper.

But most of all, the most intelligent among the canoemen, the quickest minded, the shrewdest observers, or perhaps some man already set apart as a priest, brought back ideas. Nothing was ever more contagious or spread more quickly across that continent of Indians than styles in ideas, in religions, in religious cults, introduced by a messiah-figure. What the canoes brought back now was an increased attention to the burial of the dead.

From the beginning there must have been fear of the dead, developed with the developing subtlety of the human mind. The death of a man, that incomprehensible stoppage of the breath, was an evil which must be caused by evil from those forces by which in every living moment he was surrounded. So there must be ways of dealing with that evil, as men had found ways of meeting other sorts of danger.

The care of the dead was related to the beginning of his belief in the soul, a small struggling center of power in him, more carefully to be guarded than his life. Everything he saw about him in nature had a soul, a center of power, from which his own soul was in peril.

They had great courage. They came of people who had lived hard and savage lives and their children were not weakened.

For that reason, very early in the history of the Indian, wherever the unknown stood ranged about his life, wherever birth was, and death after all, and every chance and change that can come to man and woman in their progress between the two; and against all unexplainable things, the fall of stars in the night, and lightnings, and the cry of birds, and the terrible force of the sun, and the wind that is the breath in a man's nostrils, and the spirit in his body, there this puny and naked creature who walked erect among the beasts and knew himself as something other than they, set up his beliefs and his rituals. It was the beginning of his religion.

It was concerned flatly with good and evil toward himself. It had nothing to do with morality or ethics. By words, gestures, sacrifices and appeasements, by the council of wise men nearer to the great powers than common, he was determined to seek safety. If in his progress in time and in the world he groped toward a sense of Power beyond all thronging minor powers, it was still a groping, something the ordinary man could not approach, or speak of, or try too closely to understand.

So the care of the dead grew important.

It must have been a thing for which the Indians' minds were ready. The dead were not now to be covered up and forgotten in old kitchen middens. They were buried farther away from the villages of the living, in mounds devoted entirely to burial. Such mounds were made of the local material, shells on the far islands by the mangroves of the west, sand by the lake and the moonvine-covered jungles, and rock by the wide bays of the east coast, and rock down on the lower keys.

The bodies were buried straight, as they always had been, or they were tightly flexed, knees to breast and arms crossed and head bent, a position a man takes in utter weariness, the position he held, unborn, in the oblivion of his mother's body. Or, finally, in a most curious new fashion brought here in long, slow stages from the Gulf coast, the flesh was boiled from the bones, and the bones tied together and buried in the rising mounds, above the bones of older generations.

Only at the northern edge of the Glades, where the people learned the habits of those neighbors, were there many "grave goods," the pots and spear points the dead might need. The burial mounds of all the rest of the Glades were filled with nothing but bones. Growing trees might thrust up a skull, the tender bones of a child's rib. That was all.

They heaped the mounds higher, with those heavy conch-shell picks, especially about the coasts where the high moon tides came gleaming and lipping about the house pilings, and the storms drove the white water foaming through the villages. They had already begun to dig ditches or channels across sand between sea and inlet so that a man could paddle his canoe almost to his own house platform, or so that the fish or turtles might be driven into ponds, like corrals, later a "crawl," to be caught at leisure. Such fishponds, silted up with debris and dead fish, offered rich soil for their first vegetables. There is an ancient name for "fishpond," which later was thought to mean "vegetable garden."

In this region within the sea and the lake the power of single chiefs must have grown greater. They were absolute rulers. A sort of caste system developed: chiefs and warriors, priests, craftsmen and people. The weak, the less intelligent, the handicapped, the captives of the constant border raids, were used as slave labor.

They were set to building an elaborate new system of mounds, courts, plazas and canals set apart for religious ceremonials on some important site. A round mound would be separated by a plaza from a mound curved about it in a long crescent. Or there would be numbers of round or oblong mounds with canals between. Their tops would be surmounted with altars or temples, of cabbage palm posts, probably, roofed with the inevitable palmetto thatch. Log steps would reach up to them, or there would be long ramps of the regional material, sand, or shell, or rock, where priestly professionals in torchlight would move from the massed dances on the plaza to the sound of drums.

Pine Island in the wide sea mouth of the Caloosahatchee was such a site, and the sixteen major mounds and ramps of Big Mound City near Canal Point, now on the lake. North of the Ortona Locks, among the dark pines that have grown up about it, there is a huge ceremonial moundsite. At Naples, where some of the first middens were, there was a mile-long canal across the beach.

The sweating slaves with picks were put to digging other canals, unbelievably straight, bulkheaded with cabbage palm boles, which led across islands, or from one inner channel of a mangrove river to another, so that the long canoes could go swiftly and in shelter about the coasts. Many of the later Indians kept these canals open for their travels. They were from one to six miles long, and may be traced now in half-obliterated indentations.

The Glades people had been expert woodworkers from the first, felling and hollowing cypress logs for the canoes that made their way of life possible.

Now for the ceremonials, which must have been carried on by different clans, like secret societies, perhaps each to its own mound in a group of mounds, each with its totem figure from which to gain special magic power, the woodcarvers made wonderful things. They carved animal masks for the heads of the priestly dancers, heads with movable ears and jaws, painted, with staring shell eyes. Some were stylized human faces, some were brilliant elaborated heads of wolves and turtles, cormorants and pelicans, sunfish and bats and wildcats and bears. With these masks the dancers often wore polished hollowed antlers of deer.

Smaller figures like the masks were made to be kept in the clan lodges or the houses of cult members. They were delicate and beautifully carved sitting figures, half animal, half human, and bird effigies on posts.

More striking still, they carved and painted two-foot long wooden plaques with geometric patterns superbly adapted from the totem figures. These were made with tenons by which they were set on high posts around a temple at the top of a mound, or about a whole village devoted to a particular alligator or bird cult. There were painted ceremonial tablets to be hung on the temple posts, with designs of kingfishers, or alligators,

or spiders. Some were carved with long human thigh bones, which may have been the totem of one of the new death cults. Such a cult must have used the single bowl from a lakesite, carved from the top of a human skull. It would be a thing of the greatest possible magic by which a man would gain power, as a warrior might eat the heart of a valiant enemy and so take to himself new strength.

They engraved stone to make large totem figures, like the turtle of a Tekesta clan that lay so long in a garden overlooking Biscayne Bay, and small ones, polished and carved like alligator-eye bumps.

It was only after the Spanish treasure ships began to be wrecked on the keys, or the east coast beaches brought them the white man's soft, fine copper and silver and gold, that the craftsmen adapted their old skills to metalworking. They hammered thin gold and silver plaques with incised or embossed designs, to take the place of the wooden ones on the high posts on the mounds or about a village, shining gloriously in all that sun. Sheet gold and silver was cut out and incised for small alligator tablets. They hammered out ribbons of silver for headbands, and rolled thin strips into long beads, and made concave embossed disks of gold to hang around their necks among the pierced blackened pearls and shell pendants.

The Glades people were the only ones anywhere to take a broad Spanish silver coin, cut a hole in it, and patiently hammer it into a small tube, or barrel bead, to be hung with the other things.

Seven beautiful gold, silver, and copper ornaments, like thin paper cutters cut at one end into the profile of a bird, have been found, of which six came from the Glades area, where the best craftsmen lived west of the lake. They may have been the work of a single master craftsman, for a single and very limited cult. Those were all that ever have been found. One came from a mound in Glades County, from a skull bound with a silver headband, into which the long silver thing had been struck.

It was not to be expected that among the goods from the Spanish wrecks, souvenirs sent home from Spanish conquests, the gold ornaments of South American Indians would not have been snatched up by the men of the Glades. They used hollow embossed gold beads from Ecuador and articles of gold and silver from Panama and Peru. A cast gold figure from the Rio Magdalena turned up in a Glades mound. They treasured the gold turtle shells with small pendant rattles such as have been found at Oaxaca in Mexico. All those things came from the ships.

The metals marked the end of the old time.

Before that, before they knew gold and silver, in this southernmost place of the north continent, which the easterngoing man from Asia had made his own, the westgoer and the eastgoer met face to face. Each had come half around the world, in a diversity of progress that no one understands fully, in an extent of time which no one will ever comprehend.

Far away in the sun over the blue-bright waters eastward or southward some brown man. must have stared and pointed, seeing for the first time that utterly new thing, the glint of a far white sail.

Endgame

Michael Grunwald

We view this as the most important year in our history.
—Everglades Coalition, January 2000 agenda

A Time to Act

THE SLOGAN FOR THE JANUARY 2000 Everglades Coalition conference in Naples was "A Time to Act." The political climate may not have been ideal, but momentum had been building for eight years, and the coalition's leaders were convinced that 2000 would be their best chance—perhaps their last chance—to pass a restoration project. It was also the decision year for the Homestead airport, the most prominent threat to the ecosystem in a generation. "Action taken to restore the Everglades in the next year will set the course for the next several decades," the agenda said.

Over the course of the twentieth century, Florida conservationists had helped stop plume hunts, preserve millions of acres of wetlands, mandate minimum flows to Everglades National Park, and secure the largest nutrient cleanup in history. But the Everglades was still dying. The ecosystem's natural balance was so out of whack that efforts to save the Cape Sable sparrow threatened the survival of the Everglade snail kite. Cattails were still spreading, tree islands were vanishing, muck soils were shrinking, estuaries were collapsing, and development was blocking the recharge of the region's groundwater. The greatest enemy of the Everglades, the coalition's leaders declared, was further delay.

* * *

SENATOR CHAFEE HAD PROMISED to hold a field hearing on the Comprehensive Everglades Restoration Plan at the Naples conference, and Senator Smith agreed to respect his late predecessor's wishes. Everglades activists were not expecting much from the John Birch Society's top-rated senator; after he took over the committee, the Sierra Club attacked him as "a fox in charge of the henhouse," and one journalist wrote that "many environmental groups are predicting an apocalypse of sorts." They never dreamed he would be one of the Everglades plan's most aggressive champions.

"John Chafee was strongly committed to seeing this restoration effort go forward," Smith said in his opening statement. "I totally agree. You will find no daylight between Senator Chafee's position and my own." The crowd gasped, and then cheered. Smith was a devout Roman Catholic, and he believed in the sanctity of life—not only for unborn children, but for egrets and otters, too. His six-year-old son had seen his first alligator on a vacation in the Everglades, and Smith now saw the swamp as a test for mankind: "When our distant descendants move into the Fourth Millennium, I hope it will be remembered that this generation, at the beginning of the Third Millennium, put aside partisanship, narrow self-interest and short-term thinking by saving the Everglades." Smith was as conservative as it got in American politics, but he figured that part of conservatism meant conserving things.

Senator Smith's witnesses were divided over the details of CERP, especially the Chief's Report's elevation of nature over people. But every key witness supported the Restudy. U.S. Sugar's Bubba Wade distanced the sugar industry from Citizens for a Sound Economy, and said growers now welcomed the restoration plan. Nathaniel Reed, the Everglades Coalition's elder statesman, answered the question of whether the plan would work with "an unequivocal yes!" Even Dexter Lehtinen, who devoted most of his testimony to Miccosukee grievances against the Interior Department, praised the Army Corps technical plan. Governor Bush's environmental secretary, David Struhs, quoted Senator Holland's remarks after the passage of the original C&SF Project: "The whole Florida delegation has stuck together in this matter and will, I am sure, continue to do so. The Florida citizens, industries and public units have also cooperated to the fullest degree, as has the Republican delegation. I want you to remember that this is not a partisan project, and should continue to merit the united efforts of all our people."

"That quote is as applicable in 2000 as it was in 1948," Struhs said.

The Everglades Coalition couldn't have scripted a much better start for its push for action. The restoration plan suddenly seemed sacrosanct; Senator Inhofe was the only politician who publicly opposed it, and he had no power over it. Even Senator Voinovich declared that he supported it despite his concerns about its cost and uncertainty; to be safe, Smith decided to yank the plan out of Voinovich's subcommittee and oversee it himself. "Both parties are sticking to the we-love-the-Everglades script," the *Palm Beach Post* said. Clinton administration officials met with Bush's aides in Naples, and were pleasantly surprised to hear that the governor felt as strongly as they did about swift action. Allison DeFoor, Bush's Everglades czar, called 2000 a "do-or-die year," and vowed that Florida would fund its share of CERP by the end of the spring.

DeFoor sensed that south Florida's interest groups were like drunks at the end of a bar fight. Their arms felt heavy, and they wanted an excuse to stop slugging. DeFoor set up a meeting between Audubon activists and sugar growers at Paul Tudor Jones's estate on the Keys, and both sides agreed over stone crabs to support the governor's funding bill. But the good feelings went only so far; a U.S. Sugar executive could not resist stealing one of Jones's prize orchids before he left.

BEFORE THE NAPLES CONFERENCE ENDED, Secretary Babbitt—back in good graces with his old antagonists in the Everglades Coalition—provided a final jolt of welcome news, announcing his personal opposition to the Homestead airport. A recent draft of the Clinton administration's revised study had suggested that the airport was back on track, but EPA Administrator Browner now came out against it as well. The administration was clearly divided, which meant the decision would be made in the White House.

Alan Farago, the Sierra Club activist leading the airport opposition, always figured the fight would come down to raw politics. Dade County's backroom deals reminded him of the corruption in his hometown of Providence, with Cubans instead of Italians calling the shots. But Farago believed the influence-peddlers could be defeated—not by playing kissy-face with decision-makers, but by building so much public revulsion to the airport that decision-makers would be afraid to approve it. He had quit an Audubon board out of disgust with the group's insider compromises, and he wanted to show that principled grass-roots activism could produce results.

Farago faced an uphill battle. Dade County Mayor Alex Penelas, the most prominent Cuban-American Democrat, was the airport's leading supporter. And Jorge Mas Santos, the leader of the Cuban American National Foundation—the anti-Castro group that dominated Miami exile politics—was one of the airport's key investors. President Clinton had won Florida in 1996 by making new inroads among Cuban voters and donors, and Vice President Gore's advisers feared that alienating Penelas, Mas, and the Latin Builders Association—not to mention Senator Graham—would doom his chances in Florida in 2000. Gore was already scrambling to distance himself from the Clinton administration's handling of Elián González, the five-year-old shipwreck survivor who had become a figure of religious devotion in Little Havana. Some Cuban-American leaders felt just as strongly about the Homestead issue; in fact, rumors were flying that they had offered the boy to the administration in exchange for a guarantee of the airport.

The airport's opponents also faced a serious cash disadvantage. The developers were paying more than $1 million to one of Washington's top lobbying firms, Verner, Liipfert, whose partners included former Senate Majority Leaders Bob Dole and George Mitchell. They also bankrolled an "Equal Justice Coalition," which spread the word that airport opponents were racists who wanted to keep minorities in poverty. The Sierra Club could barely afford buttons and T-shirts. But Farago noticed that Dade County's flight plans for the new airport passed directly over the Ocean Reef Club, a north Key Largo enclave of two thousand of America's wealthiest snowbirds. On his first visit, he met an elderly investor named Lloyd Schumaker, who wrote him a $100,000 check before he could even finish explaining why he was there. When Farago explained that the donation would not be tax-deductible, the crotchety Schumaker said he didn't care; he had already made $30 million that year.

Ocean Reef's residents ultimately decided to tax themselves to provide Farago with a $2 million war chest. That was enough to launch a sophisticated campaign, with pollsters, lobbyists, economic consultants, a Cuban-American community organizer, and slick ads depicting a flock of jets flying over Biscayne Bay, under the caption: Somehow, It's Not Quite the Same. The basic message was that it made no sense for the federal government to green-light a major airport at the edge of the Everglades at the same time it wanted taxpayers to spend $8 billion to restore the Everglades.

The campaign soon converted Senator Voinovich to its cause, partly because Ocean Reef was home to a number of well-connected Ohio Republicans, partly because the senator wanted to prove he cared about the Everglades despite his skepticism about the restoration plan. The usually mild-mannered Senator Mack once yelled at him to mind his own business, but Voinovich believed that if the Everglades was really "America's Everglades," as the Florida senators kept calling it, then a threat to the Everglades was America's business.

The main target of the campaign was Al Gore, who had the power to kill or approve the airport. But the vice president refused to take a stand—even after Babbitt and Browner sided with environmentalists, even after former senator Bill Bradley, his challenger for the Democratic presidential nomination, came out against the airport as well. Gore would only pledge to seek "a balanced solution" that would help the economy without harming the environment. As a public servant, Gore was often far ahead of his colleagues on issues like nuclear proliferation, environmental protection, and the "information superhighway," but as a politician, he had a tendency to straddle.

Gore's aides assumed that Florida activists would forgive him for taking a pass; after all, he had demanded the additional study that held up the airport in 1997, and had spearheaded the plan to restore the Everglades. But the airport's opponents kept up the pressure. In February, they threatened to protest an "Environmental Voters for Gore" rally in Broward County, scheduled to feature Browner with actors Leonardo DiCaprio and Ted Danson. The Gore campaign was afraid of man-bites-dog articles about conservationists attacking the Ozone Man, so the rally was cancelled. "Al Gore spilled blood for these people for eight years, and they were going to protest?" recalled Mitchell Berger, a Fort Lauderdale attorney and Democratic fund-raiser who was Gore's closest confidant in Florida. "Talk about the death of common sense."

Politically, Gore was walking a fine line between Democratic-leaning environmentalists and Republican-leaning Cuban-Americans. But the airport's opponents assumed he would return to his green roots after the predawn raid of April 22, when armed federal agents seized Elián from his Miami relatives so that his father could take him back to Cuba. There was

no way Gore could distance himself from the administration now; Nathaniel Reed told the vice president's aides he wouldn't win the Cuban vote if he promised to land the 82nd Airborne in Havana. And it was hard to imagine that Gore still cared about Mayor Penelas, who had made national headlines by declaring that the administration would be responsible if Miami rioted over Elián.

Yet Gore remained on the fence. He wasn't convinced that the airport was central to the plumbing problems that were destroying the Everglades. Neither one of his most trusted Everglades advisers, Berger and Paul Tudor Jones, had raised alarms about the airport; in fact, Berger did legal work for the Mas family, and had once told environmentalists that he could engineer a buyout of the Eight-and-a-Half Square Mile Area if they would back off the airport. Berger helped persuade Gore that the airport opposition had more to do with not-in-my-backyard complaints about noise over Ocean Reef—a vacation getaway for prominent Republicans such as Senate Appropriations Chairman Ted Stevens of Alaska—than ecological concern for the River of Grass. "I didn't think the airport threatened the survival of the Everglades," Gore later recalled. In any case, Gore's advisers figured Everglades activists would back him regardless of Homestead. Shouldn't an $8 billion restoration plan count for something?

"Consensus Was the Only Way to Do This"

BUT MANY EVERGLADES ACTIVISTS remained skeptical of the restoration plan. They had grudgingly agreed to support it after the Chief's Report provided the additional commitments that it would actually restore the Everglades. But it soon became clear that the additional commitments in the Chief's Report were dead on arrival on Capitol Hill. Senators Mack and Graham—as well as Vice President Gore and Governor Bush—believed that passing CERP depended on maintaining a consensus among Florida's interest groups, and there was a consensus among every group except environmentalists that the Clinton administration had unfairly elevated nature over people. "They wrote us a letter," an aide to Mack assured Dexter Lehtinen. "We'll write them back a law."

The nonenvironmental interests all argued that the Chief's Report—especially its guarantee of 79 billion extra gallons for the park—had violated the consensus process that produced the original technical plan.

Even Audubon's Tom Adams, the most active Everglades Coalition lobbyist, was sympathetic to the accusations of an end-run. Senators Mack and Graham wrote a letter protesting the guarantee, and the Clinton administration quickly backed off, saying the Corps was only committed to studying whether to provide the extra water. In the spring, Senate staffers agreed that their bill would ignore the Chief's Report, authorizing only the original Army Corps technical plan—the same technical plan that had been lambasted by the scientists at Everglades National Park. After months of cheerleading for CERP, the Everglades Coalition once again had to decide what to do about an Everglades restoration plan with questionable benefits for the Everglades.

The activists who had persuaded the Democratic administration to add environmental commitments to the Chief's Report hoped they could now persuade the Republican-controlled Senate to add environmental assurances to the actual bill, especially legal requirements that would reserve water for the Everglades and ensure ecological progress within a decade. They also wanted to maximize the power of the Department of the Interior, which tended to side with the environment, and minimize the power of the governor of Florida, who tended to side with his constituents. Unfortunately for the environmentalists, every other key stakeholder wanted the opposite. Sugar growers, home builders, water utilities, and Florida's other economic interests were all determined to make sure CERP did not favor nature over people—by eliminating or weakening environmental assurances, minimizing the power of Interior, and maximizing the power of the state. They had such a common vision for CERP that they shared the same Washington lobbyist, Robert Dawson, a courtly Alabama native who had overseen the Corps during the Reagan administration. Dawson did not mind if CERP was marketed as a pure Everglades restoration plan, but he warned that it would never get out of the bog without solid guarantees for water supply and flood control.

The Seminole and Miccosukee tribes agreed with Dawson's clients that CERP should not favor nature over Floridians. They may have considered the Everglades their mother, but they were Floridians, too, with their own economic interests; the Seminoles ran a $500-million-a-year gaming business as well as cattle and citrus operations, and the Miccosukees had just opened their own casino overlooking the Everglades. The Miccosukees were especially determined to limit the role of Interior, an institution they

despised. They still considered Everglades National Park their rightful homeland, and tensions had flared again recently when park leaders tried to stop them from building homes along the Tamiami Trail. Dexter Lehtinen warned that if CERP gave Interior any power over water management in Florida, "we will put a knife in the heart of this bill."

Governor Bush also sided with the economic interests. Florida's legislature had agreed to pay half of CERP's cost without a single dissenting vote, and Bush was determined to make sure equal money meant equal power. That meant an equal balance between the Everglades and his constituents, and an equal partnership between the Corps and the state; anything less, he told Congress, would be a "master-servant relationship." Senators Graham and Mack, who were in charge of refining CERP to ensure a consensus among Florida's interest groups, tended to agree. With green groups on one side and just about everyone else on the other side, it would be easier to forge consensus by pressuring the green groups to make concessions than by pressuring everyone else.

Even within the Clinton administration, there was only limited support for trying to strengthen the bill's environmental assurances. Vice President Gore had no desire to dive into details; Mitchell Berger had told him the environmental critics were extremists who would only be satisfied if the city of Weston was reflooded. Army Corps officials generally sided with Bush and the Florida interests; they didn't want to share power with Interior, and they didn't want their hands tied by restoration requirements. And George Frampton, the former Interior official who now coordinated policy at the Clinton White House, was tired of the Everglades Coalition's whining. He just wanted to pass a bill. The only administration official willing to fight was Secretary Babbitt, who didn't care too much about the details of the plumbing, but did care about Interior's role. In March, when Frampton was about to agree to strip Interior's power over CERP, Babbitt faxed a heated letter to his former aide threatening to oppose the administration's pet project if the Corps and the state retained full control: "Otherwise we allow a future that repeats past mistakes, with grievous consequences for our children and grandchildren." Frampton backed down, and the internal split never became public.

It was the threat of a public showdown that gave Babbitt his leverage within the administration; Vice President Gore did not want to be blamed for delaying the revival of the Everglades before the election. But the

Everglades Coalition did not have much leverage in the Senate to demand benefits for the environment. The coalition had secured the commitments in the Chief's Report by threatening to oppose CERP, but those threats were a lot less credible now that it had declared 2000 "A Time to Act," and national conservation organizations were clamoring for Congress to pass the bill. Environmentalists who still hoped to improve the bill could see that their chances were shrinking by the day, as Audubon and other groups began jockeying to portray themselves to funders as the saviors of the Everglades. There was intense pressure to stay "on message," to stop quibbling over details, to avoid discrediting CERP. Audubon issued one statement declaring that "we will continue to seek improvements in the bill to increase restoration benefits—as long as they do not endanger its enactment."

"Our feeling was: This isn't perfect, but it's more good than bad," said Audubon president John Flicker. Even CERP's water-supply components would reduce pressure on the Everglades, and several uncontroversial restoration components would benefit Big Cypress, the St. Lucie estuary, and Biscayne Bay's coastal wetlands. The Wall Street wizard Paul Tudor Jones told Audubon leaders that he had spent $5 million on the Everglades; he would consider $8 billion an excellent return. Larry Kast, a brash young water resources lobbyist who joined the Audubon team during CERP, advised environmentalists to stop trying to sweeten the deal. "I was focused like a laser beam on getting this passed, and the key was unity in Florida," Kast recalled. "We had to stop arguing over every frigging detail and every frigging drop of water. We had to get our shit together, or we were going to lose $8 billion."

More skeptical activists such as Environmental Defense's Tim Searchinger and NRDC's Brad Sewell knew that some of their colleagues believed they were threatening a fragile consensus, turning up their noses at an $8 billion restoration plan because it wasn't perfect. But this was the same plan the park's scientists had said "does not represent a restoration scenario for the southern, central and northern Everglades." The latest version of CERP did not even guarantee that the project would do no harm to the Everglades—only that no one's level of water supply or flood control would be reduced. That seemed a lot worse than imperfect.

ON MAY 11, Chairman Smith and Senator Max Baucus of Montana, the ranking Democrat on Smith's committee, held the first hearing on the Ever-

glades bill. It was supposed to be a typical congressional Kabuki show, an opportunity for flowery speeches about the majesty of the River of Grass, with Smith demonstrating the Republican commitment to restoration and Baucus carrying water for the Clinton plan. But as Baucus listened to testimony about the plan's "tremendous amount of flexibility"—and watched witnesses duck questions about its ecological uncertainties—he did something exceedingly rare in Washington. He ditched his script and spoke his mind:

> I'm a little uneasy and I'll tell you why. I worry about seeing the evening news a year or two or three from now, "The Fleecing of America," "It's Your Money," something like that. . . . I have a funny feeling that I might be buying something that sounds good, but down the road, it's going to leave my successors a huge, huge program. And the problem is, we've spent all this money on the Everglades and my gosh, it's not working like it was supposed to work. Oh, we've gone this far, gee, it's like the Vietnam War in a sense, we've got to keep pouring more money into it because it's gone this far. What's our exit strategy?

An aide to the senator kept passing him notes and kicking his chair, but Baucus kept rambling. "Nobody has provided a compelling case that this is going to work," he blurted. "So far, it doesn't totally pass the smell test, if you want the honest truth."

This unplanned outburst of candor offered unexpected ammunition to Searchinger, Sewell, and other environmental critics of the restoration bill. They contended that without strict legal assurances for the natural system, Florida officials would keep giving away water needed for the Everglades to cities and farms, and CERP would never pass the smell test needed to secure national support. Governor Bush's lobbyists argued that assurances were unnecessary, because Florida already had the power to reserve water for the environment. But the state had only used that power once in twenty-eight years, for a marsh in the St. Johns basin. Senate staffers were wary of fixes that would antagonize every lobby except the enviros, but most of them—especially Senator Smith's aides—eventually realized the critics had a point. CERP had to change the status quo that had destroyed the Everglades.

The problem was finding the right language that could nail down the support of queasy environmentalists and avoid "Fleecing of America" exposés without losing the support of the other interest groups. After months of roller-coaster negotiations, Florida's economic interests withdrew their support for the bill in early August, then changed their minds after extracting a few key concessions. In early September, Senators Graham and Mack orchestrated a settlement of every key group, only to see Governor Bush's aides pull out of the agreement. This time, Senator Mack called Bush and explained that the state of Florida was holding up an excellent compromise. The governor, who was campaigning for his brother out west, called his underlings and told them to back down. George W. Bush didn't want to be blamed for scuttling Everglades restoration, either.

Anyway, Jeb Bush had gotten most of what he wanted in the bill. The state would be an equal partner with the Corps, which was already sympathetic to Florida's economic interests. Interior would only have a veto over the rules governing the project, not the sixty-eight project components. Those rules would not define the natural system's water needs, as environmentalists had hoped; they would only set up "a process" to define those needs. (Bush's aides had tried to dilute the rules even further, proposing that they set up "a process to provide procedural guidance" to define those needs.) Senator Voinovich secured a resolution declaring that reuse of the Homestead air base should be compatible with Everglades restoration, but Graham and Mack fought off substantive measures that could have blocked the proposed airport. Nobody's ox would be gored by CERP.

In general, the assurances did not assure much for the Everglades, although they did impose a few restraints on state water managers. The bill stated that "the overarching purpose" of the bill was restoration, but its substantive provisions included much stronger protections for flood control and water supply. And while Senator Smith's aides did jam some extra assurances language into their committee report, highlighting the Army Corps pledge that 80 percent of the water captured by CERP would go to the environment, the report did not have the force of law.

A few environmental groups denounced the consensus legislation, most notably Friends of the Everglades, the grass-roots organization founded by Marjory Stoneman Douglas. Robert Johnson, the head of Everglades National Park's science staff, told the *Washington Post* that the legislation would do almost nothing for the environment: "This is just a situation

where the emperor has no clothes." When Audubon, the National Parks Conservation Association, the National Wildlife Federation, and Defenders of Wildlife passed around a draft letter describing CERP as a "must-pass" bill, the ecologist Stuart Pimm wrote a blistering critique:

> Of course, we should all live long and healthy lives; we will need to do so if we are to see this plan's benefits. . . . I can see why the sugar growers like this plan. This is a plan for ecological inaction and that is exactly why I find fault with it. I believe that consensus is fine. I applaud your efforts to work out compromise. But at some level this must fail: just because the policymakers all agree that the sun rises in the west doesn't make it so.

But most green groups went along with the deal—some with trepidation, some with enthusiasm. "This is an historic agreement for the future of America's Everglades," rejoiced Audubon's Stuart Strahl. Johnson's bosses at Interior also endorsed the bill, along with the rest of the Clinton administration. Secretary Babbitt would have preferred solid guarantees for the natural system, but he figured all the hype over "America's Everglades" would at least create expectations of restoration in the future. Perhaps the sugar industry would agree to sacrifice more land for restoration after it exhausted its soils, or after it lost its federal price protections, or after Castro died. Perhaps prolonged water shortages—and the rate hikes that could accompany them—would persuade Floridians to start conserving their most precious resource. Or maybe desalinization or some other new technology would solve south Florida's water problems. CERP would just be a start.

The Everglades Is Coming

THE PLAN WAS NOW IN PLACE, but Congress still had to approve it before adjourning for the election. Army Corps bills tend to pass at the last minute without debate, because Congress prefers to keep its pork platters off C-SPAN. But this one still had to make it through the Senate and House. "The single greatest threat to restoration of America's Everglades is the lack of time left in the congressional session," said Audubon's Strahl.

Behind the scenes, Florida's state officials, economic interests, and tribes had all fought to reduce CERP's emphasis on nature, but they now came together to promote it as a restoration plan for America's Everglades. Audubon lobbyist Tom Adams walked the halls of Congress arm-in-arm with sugar lobbyist Bob Dawson. "If we can agree to support the Everglades," they told members, "then you should, too." Senators Smith and Mack rallied support among Republicans, while Senator Graham and the Clinton administration lined up Democrats. It wasn't too hard. When Senator Inhofe tried to persuade colleagues that CERP was an astronomically expensive, scandalously uncertain exercise in government bloat, they often replied: But it's the Everglades! Senate Majority Leader Trent Lott had no great interest in the Everglades—he joked that he was pretty sure it wasn't in Mississippi—but he fast-tracked the Corps bill as a favor to Mack.

One potential sticking point was a raging debate over "Corps reform." After a Corps economist blew the whistle on the agency's frantic efforts to justify a billion-dollar lock project on the Mississippi River, Corps follies became front-page fodder, and Corps critics called for independent reviews of major projects, setting the stage for an ugly floor fight. But the environmental establishment never pressed too hard for the reforms, because it did not want to endanger Everglades restoration. So the Corps bill went to the Senate floor without them.

Instead, the Senate debate over the bill was dominated by florid tributes to the Everglades, and to the bipartisan consensus that had brought together Florida's Hatfields and McCoys. Senator Smith read a list of endorsers ranging from the Florida Fertilizer and Agrichemical Association to the National Parks Conservation Association. Senator Graham marveled at how much had changed since he launched his Save Our Everglades program to turn back time in south Florida. "In 1983, restoring the natural health and function of this precious system seemed to be a distant dream," he said. "After seventeen years of bipartisan progress, we now stand on the brink of this dream becoming a reality." But Senators Inhofe and Voinovich were not the only voices of caution. Senator John Warner, a Republican from Virginia, complained that the Everglades would dwarf all other water projects, including the restoration of Chesapeake Bay. "All of a sudden, we come along with the romance of the Everglades," Warner said. "Paul Revere called out: The British are coming. I call out: Folks, this is coming. You better go back home and talk to your constituents and say this one is going to be in competition with what I had planned for our state." Senator Baucus

tried to defend the bill, but he again betrayed his doubts, acknowledging that part of him agreed with the critics. "This arrangement may not be perfect," Baucus said. "But we are dealing with an extraordinary, special situation, and that is the Everglades. . . . There is a slight tilt in favor of the State of Florida, but the Everglades is really special. It is a national treasure."

The Senate passed the bill by an 85 to 1 margin, with Inhofe the only dissenter. "If you have any doubts about every single 'i' being dotted and every 't' being crossed, take the risk. You'll be glad you did," Smith said. "When the historians look back, they are going to say when it came time to stand up for the Everglades, we did."

Now the House of Representatives controlled the fate of the Everglades. Momentous issues were at stake—the most ambitious ecosystem restoration in history, a new model for dealing with water conflicts, a new direction for the Corps, a chance to prove that man could repair his relationship with Mother Nature. But in the House, only one issue mattered: Clay Shaw was in a tight race. The workmanlike ten-term congressman from Fort Lauderdale was one of the most vulnerable Republicans, and with control of the House hanging on a few contested races, Speaker Dennis Hastert of Illinois was willing to do anything necessary to help the chairman of the Florida delegation. "We knew this could come down to two seats, and if that meant we had to spend $8 billion for Mr. Shaw, that's what we were going to do," one Hastert aide recalled.

In September, Shaw introduced the Senate's Everglades deal in the House, and Chairman Shuster attached it to an Army Corps bill that was so crammed with local water projects it took up forty-five pages of the *Congressional Record*. The bill had been held up all summer in a partisan dispute over prevailing-wage laws, but Republicans now agreed to drop their objections to get the Altoonaglades passed. On October 19, Shaw presided over the debate from the speaker's chair, watched a series of Republicans give him credit for saving the Everglades, and made the final speech before the House approved the bill by a 394 to 14 margin. "We are seeing a rare moment in the closing days of this Congress: both great political parties coming together and doing the right thing," Shaw crowed.

THE CONGRESSIONAL DEBATE over the Everglades was dominated by high-minded rhetoric about the River of Grass being above partisan politics. But it was still election season, and Florida was shaping up as the key battleground between Vice President Gore and George W. Bush. The day before the House voted on CERP, Gore's campaign aides huddled with Everglades activists in Miami, pleading with them to rally their troops behind the vice president. Kathleen McGinty, Gore's top environmental adviser, began the meeting by pointing out that Gore had led the fight to restore the Everglades, taken on the sugar industry over penny-a-pound, and fought for the environment all his life. But all the activists wanted to talk about was his waffling on the Homestead airport.

The Gore campaign had never imagined that they would have to beg Florida environmentalists for support three weeks before Election Day. George W. Bush was the dream candidate of drilling, mining, and logging interests; Gore was their nightmare. When a Democratic operative had tried to warn Gore campaign manager Donna Brazile that Everglades activists were irate about Homestead, the message had come back: "Tell them to go fuck themselves." Where else could environmentalists turn?

The answer, for some of them, had been Ralph Nader, the consumer crusader who was running on the Green Party ticket, attacking Bush and Gore as twin peas in a corporate pod. Joe Browder, a lifelong Democrat, had begun feeding information on Homestead to the Nader campaign and a group called Environmentalists Against Gore, and Nader had started making speeches denouncing the airport plan and accusing Gore of selling out the Everglades. Alan Farago had refused to take Nader's calls, but he knew the airport was costing Gore votes. In September, he had commissioned a Democratic pollster to conduct a survey of Florida voters, which suggested that Gore would gain four points if he came out against the airport. The Sierra Club had given the results to Gore's campaign, but the vice president refused to switch his position.

Even Nathaniel Reed, the ultimate inside player, had grown exasperated after months of behind-the-scenes lobbying against the airport. The vice president's aides had promised Reed that he would make an anti-airport speech, and Reed tended to err on the side of trust, especially with eco-friendly politicians like the Ozone Man. But he eventually realized that Gore had no intention of getting off the fence, and he fired off an e-mail throughout the environmental community, warning that Gore was contemplating the destruction of two beloved parks. "Until the Administration and in particular the Vice President is confronted with opposition, the Administration will continue to ignore the issue," Reed wrote. "From crisis comes opportunity! Force the crisis!"

Now it was three weeks before the election, and the Gore campaign realized it had a Nader crisis in south Florida. McGinty, Gore confidant Mitchell Berger, and former water management district director Sam Poole were dispatched to try to persuade the enviros that Homestead was a crazy litmus test. McGinty argued that Gore had gone to bat for the environment for his entire career; it was time for environmentalists to go to bat for Gore. But the activists just wanted to know why he had stayed in the on-deck circle on the airport. They said his silence was driving their members to Nader.

Berger couldn't believe he was having this conversation. George W. Bush hadn't taken a position on the airport. Neither had Jeb Bush. And Gore at least had an excuse for staying mum; the administration's study was still under way, and taking sides could be construed as interference. Anyway, Gore had intervened to block the initial pro-airport study; didn't that suggest his true feelings? Babbitt and Browner publicly opposed the airport; didn't that suggest where the decision was headed? If Gore made a statement now, it would just look like pandering. "Isn't there any trust in this room?" Berger asked.

There wasn't much. One airport opponent challenged Berger on his work for Jorge Mas; Berger insisted it didn't matter. McGinty said Gore wanted to hold an environmental rally in south Florida to highlight his defense of the Everglades, and asked whether there would be protesters. Absolutely, she was told. "Tell him that only a true friend will tell you what you don't want to hear," one activist said. "And what you don't want to hear is that you are going to lose this election because of Homestead."

MEANWHILE, the Everglades plan was in danger yet again. The House and Senate had to reconcile their Army Corps bills, and Senator Smith objected to a half-billion dollars of "environmental infrastructure" in the House bill. He knew "environmental infrastructure" was a euphemism for water and sewer plants, which were supposed to be local responsibilities. The Corps was already under fire for General Ballard's "Program Growth Initiative," and Smith didn't want to encourage more mission creep. He told Chairman Shuster he would block the bill unless the extra pork was removed.

Shuster was flabbergasted. A committee chairman objecting to the presence of pork in a Corps bill was like a Burger King fry cook objecting to the presence of beef in a Whopper. Environmental infrastructure was especially dear to Shuster's heart; he had invented the concept in a 1992 bill, diverting the first projects to his own district, then authorizing billions of dollars' worth of additional projects for other members. He was appalled by Smith's selfishness, and House Speaker Hastert was even angrier. Several vulnerable Republicans were counting on environmental infrastructure projects to build support at home before Election Day, and Shaw was counting on CERP, but Smith didn't seem to care who controlled Congress.

Only in Washington could an effort to save taxpayer dollars be considered selfish, but Smith's sudden stand on principle did seem odd. He had agreed to a bill with 138 water projects worth $7 billion, not including the Everglades behemoth, which as far as Shuster concerned was just another huge water project. Smith hadn't objected to flood protection for East Saint Louis or the renourishment of Rehoboth Beach or a comprehensive study of the Merrimack River basin in his home state of New Hampshire. Why was he drawing a line in the sand over sewer projects that actually helped people? Smith was hauled into a meeting with Speaker Hastert, and the avuncular former wrestling coach got as livid as his aides had ever seen him, throwing his pen in Smith's direction. "This is bullshit!" Hastert screamed. But Smith refused to budge. He found it hard to believe that a few sewage plants were going to determine the outcome of the election. "Control of the House is in Bob Smith's hands!" one of his aides wrote in a sarcastic e-mail. "Give me a break."

Congress was running out of time, so Senator Mack went to see House Appropriations Chairman C. W. "Bill" Young of Florida, who agreed to tack CERP onto an agriculture spending bill if the larger Corps bill was scuttled. Shuster realized his entire bill was in danger of stalling without its Everglades engine, so he relented and agreed to pass it without environmental infrastructure. Speaker Hastert then forced Young to tack the infrastructure projects onto a health spending bill. Nobody's ox was going to be gored on Capitol Hill.

It wasn't pretty, but four days before the election, Congress finally passed the Altoonaglades, prompting another round of speeches depicting Clay Shaw as the second coming of Marjory Stoneman Douglas. "Governor Broward, for whom my home county is named, ran on the platform that he was going to drain that swamp, the Everglades," Shaw said. "November 3 is the day we took the first step in really restoring this national treasure."

* * *

CONGRESSMAN SHAW RACED BACK to south Florida to campaign, and the Everglades headlines helped him edge his Democratic opponent by six hundred votes. Vice President Gore was not so lucky.

Ralph Nader visited Miami for a get-out-the-vote rally on November 5, and used Joe Browder's talking points to blast Gore for "waffling as usual" on the Homestead airport. "Congress and the state of Florida are poised to spend $8 billion to rehabilitate the Everglades," he said. "Why won't the Vice President take a stand against undermining these efforts?" Nader also sent letters to Florida environmentalists, bashing Gore for buckling to real estate interests: "There are no airports situated on the border of national parks in America; the Everglades is the last place to consider changing that."

Gore campaigned in Florida, too, but he never did hold that Everglades rally, and south Florida's environmentalists never did generate much enthusiasm for him. It was frustrating, but Gore always knew that for some Ivory Soap environmentalists, as he put it, "Ninety-nine and forty-four-hundredths percent pure was never good enough." He was more irritated at Mayor Penelas, who was reelected in September, then took off for a vacation in Spain, contributing nothing to Gore's campaign or his fight for a recount. After the votes were counted on Election Day, Gore trailed Bush by 537 votes in Florida. Nader received more than 96,000 votes, and some operatives attributed 10,000 of them to the airport issue. That was more than enough to elect a president who would support oil exploration in the Arctic National Wildlife Refuge, reverse his campaign promise to regulate carbon emissions, and enrage environmentalists like no president since Ronald Reagan. "Oh, I don't think the airport was a major factor in the outcome," Gore said in a recent interview.

Then he paused. "Well, maybe it was."

ON DECEMBER 11, 2000, the Gore campaign's last day in court, Senator Graham woke up in Miami Lakes at 6:05 A.M. According to his characteristically meticulous notebook, he weighed in at 187 pounds, ate some fiber cereal with raisins, and listened to six voice-mail messages. At 9:17

A.M., he flew to Washington on American Airlines flight 1394; he sat in seat 3A, and updated his notebooks for ten minutes at 10:30 A.M. After arriving in Washington, he purchased 11.833 gallons of gas at $1.599 per gallon at a Pennsylvania Avenue Amoco. Then he headed to the White House to celebrate the crowning achievement of his thirty-four-year political career. President Clinton was finally signing the Everglades bill, America's effort to restore Graham's boyhood playground, to re-create the watery wonderland that sheltered millions of wading birds before pioneers like his father began trying to tame it. For Graham, this was bigger than *Bush v. Gore*.

Graham liked to say that when Hamilton Disston first saw the panoramic sawgrass marshes of the Everglades, he must have thought: This doesn't look anything like Philadelphia. It looked strange and unique, and the young industrialist had been determined to convert it into something familiar and productive. But Graham liked strange and unique, as one might expect of a politician who recorded his breakfast choices every morning for posterity. Yes, restoring the Everglades would preserve aquifers and promote ecotourism, but Graham really wanted to restore the Everglades because it was singular, because it distinguished south Florida from other sprawling concatenations of tract homes, strip malls, CVS, and KFC. Marjory Stoneman Douglas had made that point with the first sentence of her book: "There are no other Everglades in the world." It was an American original, it was dying, and now it would receive open-heart surgery. Graham's only concern was that as years passed, billions of dollars were spent, and the patient remained critical, enthusiasm would wane, money would be diverted elsewhere, and the Everglades would be abandoned mid-operation.

Everyone at the bizarre bipartisan White House ceremony knew the Everglades still faced a multitude of threats. There were still 50,000 tons of phosphorus sitting at the bottom of Lake Okeechobee, and 2 million acres of exotic vegetation marching across the Everglades. Red tides were massacring dolphins, manatees, and sea turtles in the estuaries, while plagues and other diseases were killing off the coral reefs. Secretary Babbitt was concerned about the runaway sprawl that continued to chew up the edges of the ecosystem, forcing the Army Corps to paint its restoration masterpiece on an ever-shrinking canvas. Senator Smith threw his arm around Michael Davis, who was moving to Florida to oversee the restoration project, and gestured toward Governor Bush and his aides. "You've got to watch those guys," he whispered to Davis. "They're going to try to grab all that water." President Clinton, shooting the breeze with two legislative aides after the ceremony, flagged another dire threat: rising sea levels. "If we don't do something about climate change," he said, "your Everglades is going to be underwater."

But this was a day to imagine a better future, to reclaim the Everglades in a new way. It was now as unifying a force as it had been during the drainage era, except that the new consensus called for undraining it. While Florida was roiling over "undervotes" and "overvotes," everyone was holding hands over the swamp. "I'd be happy to speculate about the Supreme Court!" Graham told the swarm of reporters gathered outside the West Wing. He then grinned and returned to his preferred subject: "This is a very happy day for the Everglades, and a signal day for the movement around the world to try to repair damaged environmental systems." Smith pointed out that there were no alligators in New Hampshire; the Everglades seemed to transcend state lines, just as it seemed to transcend party lines. It had become a symbol of America's responsibility to make amends to Mother Nature. "We worked together to save a national treasure," Smith said. "It didn't get a lot of ink in what's going on today, but it's very, very important."

The power of the Everglades lay in its example. The twentieth century had been an era of mess-making; the twenty-first century could be a time to clean up the messes. And not just the toxic petrochemical messes that had set rivers on fire and thinned the shells of bald eagles during the sixties, but the ordinary messes created by man's routine dominion over nature. Man's efforts to tame the Everglades had taken a toll—the death tolls of the 1926 and 1928 hurricanes, the near-extinction of panthers and sparrows and gourds, the soil losses and water shortages and traffic jams on the Palmetto Expressway—but they had created homes and vacation destinations for millions of people, and more were on the way. Everglades restoration could set an international standard for sustainable development. It could prove that man and nature could coexist in peace.

After Governor Bush dodged more questions about his brother—"Marvin? He's doing well. That's very kind of you to think about him."—Babbitt stepped forward to talk about the Everglades as a model, a paradigm for thinking on a landscape scale. He suggested a partial list of endangered

American ecosystems that could follow south Florida's example: the Great Lakes, San Francisco Bay, New York Harbor, and the Missouri and Mississippi River basins.

Babbitt also mentioned the Louisiana coast, where—due largely to the enduring battle between the Corps and the Mississippi River—wetlands were disappearing at the astonishing rate of twenty-five square miles per year, decimating fish and wildlife while exposing New Orleans to storm surges. Governor Bush predicted that the ripples from the Everglades would extend even further than that: "This is a model—not just for our country, but for projects around the world."

THE UNANSWERED QUESTION WAS whether it would turn out to be a new model. Would it be a true restoration project, revamping man's approach to the Everglades, or just another dirt-moving Corps water project, "environmental infrastructure" with better press? Would it inaugurate a new relationship between the human and natural environments in south Florida, encouraging man to limit his footprint and live in harmony with the ecosystem, or would it just facilitate additional growth and sprawl, luring millions more people into the path of the next hurricane? Would politicians and engineers begin to consider the needs of birds, bears, and bays in addition to the needs of man, or would water continue to flow uphill toward money?

On the same day that President Clinton celebrated the new politics of the Everglades at the White House, while the Supreme Court prepared to choose his successor, a meeting in West Palm Beach suggested that the old politics of the Everglades was not quite dead. South Florida was suffering through one of its worst droughts ever, and Lake Okeechobee was so low that the water management district's guidelines prohibited releases for irrigation. But a consultant for the sugar industry had demanded to see the district's engineers, warning in an e-mail that "users will never sit still for zero water-supply releases." He got his meeting on December 11, and with no public input, the engineers agreed to tweak their guidelines so that growers could receive half their usual releases. That winter, the lake plunged below nine feet for the first time in recorded history. A third of the lake disappeared, along with most of its bass, and the region was battered so badly that Governor Bush declared an economic state of emergency. But the sugar industry enjoyed its fourth-largest harvest ever. "Thanks for all your work

and for continuing to improve the process," the consultant wrote to the district's engineers.

That money-talks process has damaged the Everglades for more than a century, and it has damaged ecosystems around the world. CERP is supposed to change that, by making sure there is enough water for nature and the public as well as special interests. At a time when fresh water is emerging as the oil of the twenty-first century, Everglades restoration will be a crucial test of man's ability to stave off the bloody water wars that some analysts expect to erupt in the coming decades. If south Florida can't solve problems limited to one state in the wealthiest nation on earth, with billions of dollars to spend and fifty-five annual inches of rain to distribute, it's hard to imagine solving cross-border water disputes in poorer and drier regions. And south Florida has a trump card—the Everglades, the most beloved wetland on the planet, and the most intensely studied. If man can't save the Everglades, what can he save?

Senator Graham is probably the starkest example of the Everglades dilemma. His father was a sugar grower, a cattle rancher, and a real estate developer who dreamed of draining the Everglades. Graham launched the movement to restore the Everglades. But he also continued to support sugar farming, cattle ranching, and real estate development. He wouldn't have been the most popular politician in Florida if he hadn't. In fact, Graham's notes reveal that on the afternoon of December 11, after he watched fifteen minutes of MSNBC commentary about the Supreme Court hearing but before he bought a half-gallon of low-fat milk, the senator spoke to the Cuban-American leader Jorge Mas about the Homestead airport. Graham had declared that he would remain neutral and respect the Clinton administration's final decision, but everyone knew he was still pushing for the airport.

Graham still wanted to save the Everglades; he had started Save Our Everglades. But every politician had to strike a balance between nature and people.

ON JANUARY 16, 2001, four days before Clinton left office, the administration announced its decision on Homestead. It rejected the airport. It was too late to change the Nader votes of south Florida's environmentalists, but the Everglades had dodged another bullet. It was a reminder that money doesn't always talk. People talk, too. "This is a victory for common sense and public input over special interests," one activist said. It was also a victory for hard-line Ivory Soap environmentalists over the moderates who had considered the airport war a lost cause—although the greenest vice president in history turned out to be a casualty of that war.

As the new millennium dawned, the Everglades was not yet saved. But it was not yet doomed, either. Millions of acres of the ecosystem remained in public ownership. Water quality was improving. And America was now formally committed to restoring the Everglades, with billions of dollars and the prestige of a nation on the line. That didn't mean it would happen, but it meant there was a chance.

The Earth Charter

Earth Charter Commission

PREAMBLE

We stand at a critical moment in Earth's history, a time when humanity must choose its future. As the world becomes increasingly interdependent and fragile, the future at once holds great peril and great promise. To move forward we must recognize that in the midst of a magnificent diversity of cultures and life forms we are one human family and one Earth community with a common destiny. We must join together to bring forth a sustainable global society founded on respect for nature, universal human rights, economic justice, and a culture of peace. Towards this end, it is imperative that we, the peoples of Earth, declare our responsibility to one another, to the greater community of life, and to future generations.

Earth, Our Home

Humanity is part of a vast evolving universe. Earth, our home, is alive with a unique community of life. The forces of nature make existence a demanding and uncertain adventure, but Earth has provided the conditions essential to life's evolution. The resilience of the community of life and the well-being of humanity depend upon preserving a healthy biosphere with all its ecological systems, a rich variety of plants and animals, fertile soils, pure waters, and clean air. The global environment with its finite resources is a common concern of all peoples. The protection of Earth's vitality, diversity, and beauty is a sacred trust.

The Global Situation

The dominant patterns of production and consumption are causing environmental devastation, the depletion of resources, and a massive extinction of species. Communities are being undermined. The benefits of development are not shared equitably and the gap between rich and poor is widening. Injustice, poverty, ignorance, and violent conflict are widespread and the cause of great suffering. An unprecedented rise in human population has overburdened ecological and social systems. The foundations of global security are threatened. These trends are perilous—but not inevitable.

The Challenges Ahead

The choice is ours: form a global partnership to care for Earth and one another or risk the destruction of ourselves and the diversity of life. Fundamental changes are needed in our values, institutions, and ways of living. We must realize that when basic needs have been met, human development is primarily about being more, not having more. We have the knowledge and technology to provide for all and to reduce our impacts on the environment. The emergence of a global civil society is creating new opportunities to build a democratic and humane world. Our environmental, economic, political, social, and spiritual challenges are interconnected, and together we can forge inclusive solutions.

Universal Responsibility

To realize these aspirations, we must decide to live with a sense of universal responsibility, identifying ourselves with the whole Earth community as well as our local communities. We are at once citizens of different nations and of one world in which the local and global are linked. Everyone shares responsibility for the present and future well-being of the human family and the larger living world. The spirit of human solidarity and kinship with all life is strengthened when we live with reverence for the mystery of being, gratitude for the gift of life, and humility regarding the human place in nature.

We urgently need a shared vision of basic values to provide an ethical foundation for the emerging world community. Therefore, together in hope we affirm the following interdependent principles for a sustainable way of life as a common standard by which the conduct of all individuals, organizations, businesses, governments, and transnational institutions is to be guided and assessed.

PRINCIPLES

I. RESPECT AND CARE FOR THE COMMUNITY OF LIFE

1. Respect Earth and life in all its diversity.

a. Recognize that all beings are interdependent and every form of life has value regardless of its worth to human beings.

b. Affirm faith in the inherent dignity of all human beings and in the intellectual, artistic, ethical, and spiritual potential of humanity.

2. Care for the community of life with understanding, compassion, and love.

a. Accept that with the right to own, manage, and use natural resources comes the duty to prevent environmental harm and to protect the rights of people.

b. Affirm that with increased freedom, knowledge, and power comes increased responsibility to promote the common good.

3. Build democratic societies that are just, participatory, sustainable, and peaceful.

a. Ensure that communities at all levels guarantee human rights and fundamental freedoms and provide everyone an opportunity to realize his or her full potential.

b. Promote social and economic justice, enabling all to achieve a secure and meaningful livelihood that is ecologically responsible.

4. Secure Earth's bounty and beauty for present and future generations.

a. Recognize that the freedom of action of each generation is qualified by the needs of future generations.

b. Transmit to future generations values, traditions, and institutions that support the long-term flourishing of Earth's human and ecological communities. In order to fulfill these four broad commitments, it is necessary to:

II. ECOLOGICAL INTEGRITY

5. Protect and restore the integrity of Earth's ecological systems, with special concern for biological diversity and the natural processes that sustain life.

a. Adopt at all levels sustainable development plans and regulations that make environmental conservation and rehabilitation integral to all development initiatives.

b. Establish and safeguard viable nature and biosphere reserves, including wild lands and marine areas, to protect Earth's life support systems, maintain biodiversity, and preserve our natural heritage.

c. Promote the recovery of endangered species and ecosystems.

d. Control and eradicate non-native or genetically modified organisms harmful to native species and the environment, and prevent introduction of such harmful organisms.

e. Manage the use of renewable resources such as water, soil, forest products, and marine life in ways that do not exceed rates of regeneration and that protect the health of ecosystems.

f. Manage the extraction and use of non-renewable resources such as minerals and fossil fuels in ways that minimize depletion and cause no serious environmental damage.

6. Prevent harm as the best method of environmental protection and, when knowledge is limited, apply a precautionary approach.

a. Take action to avoid the possibility of serious or irreversible environmental harm even when scientific knowledge is incomplete or inconclusive.

b. Place the burden of proof on those who argue that a proposed activity will not cause significant harm, and make the responsible parties liable for environmental harm.

c. Ensure that decision making addresses the cumulative, long-term, indirect, long distance, and global consequences of human activities.

d. Prevent pollution of any part of the environment and allow no build-up of radioactive, toxic, or other hazardous substances.

e. Avoid military activities damaging to the environment.

7. Adopt patterns of production, consumption, and reproduction that safeguard Earth's regenerative capacities, human rights, and community well-being.

a. Reduce, reuse, and recycle the materials used in production and consumption systems, and ensure that residual waste can be assimilated by ecological systems.

b. Act with restraint and efficiency when using energy, and rely increasingly on renewable energy sources such as solar and wind.

c. Promote the development, adoption, and equitable transfer of environmentally sound technologies.

d. Internalize the full environmental and social costs of goods and services in the selling price, and enable consumers to identify products that meet the highest social and environmental standards.

e. Ensure universal access to health care that fosters reproductive health and responsible reproduction.

f. Adopt lifestyles that emphasize the quality of life and material sufficiency in a finite world.

8. Advance the study of ecological sustainability and promote the open exchange and wide application of the knowledge acquired.

a. Support international scientific and technical cooperation on sustainability, with special attention to the needs of developing nations.

b. Recognize and preserve the traditional knowledge and spiritual wisdom in all cultures that contribute to environmental protection and human well-being.

c. Ensure that information of vital importance to human health and environmental protection, including genetic information, remains available in the public domain.

III. SOCIAL AND ECONOMIC JUSTICE

9. Eradicate poverty as an ethical, social, and environmental imperative.

a. Guarantee the right to potable water, clean air, food security, uncontaminated soil, shelter, and safe sanitation, allocating the national and international resources required.

b. Empower every human being with the education and resources to secure a sustainable livelihood, and provide social security and safety nets for those who are unable to support themselves.

c. Recognize the ignored, protect the vulnerable, serve those who suffer, and enable them to develop their capacities and to pursue their aspirations.

10. Ensure that economic activities and institutions at all levels promote human development in an equitable and sustainable manner.

a. Promote the equitable distribution of wealth within nations and among nations.

b. Enhance the intellectual, financial, technical, and social resources of developing nations, and relieve them of onerous international debt.

c. Ensure that all trade supports sustainable resource use, environmental protection, and progressive labor standards.

d. Require multinational corporations and international financial organizations to act transparently in the public good, and hold them accountable for the consequences of their activities.

11. Affirm gender equality and equity as prerequisites to sustainable development and ensure universal access to education, health care, and economic opportunity.

a. Secure the human rights of women and girls and end all violence against them.

b. Promote the active participation of women in all aspects of economic, political, civil, social, and cultural life as full and equal partners, decision makers, leaders, and beneficiaries.

c. Strengthen families and ensure the safety and loving nurture of all family members.

12. Uphold the right of all, without discrimination, to a natural and social environment supportive of human dignity, bodily health, and spiritual well-being, with special attention to the rights of indigenous peoples and minorities.

a. Eliminate discrimination in all its forms, such as that based on race, color, sex, sexual orientation, religion, language, and national, ethnic or social origin.

b. Affirm the right of indigenous peoples to their spirituality, knowledge, lands and resources and to their related practice of sustainable livelihoods.

c. Honor and support the young people of our communities, enabling them to fulfill their essential role in creating sustainable societies.

d. Protect and restore outstanding places of cultural and spiritual significance.

IV. DEMOCRACY, NONVIOLENCE, AND PEACE

13. Strengthen democratic institutions at all levels, and provide transparency and accountability in governance, inclusive participation in decision making, and access to justice.

a. Uphold the right of everyone to receive clear and timely information on environmental matters and all development plans and activities which are likely to affect them or in which they have an interest.

b. Support local, regional and global civil society, and promote the meaningful participation of all interested individuals and organizations in decision making.

c. Protect the rights to freedom of opinion, expression, peaceful assembly, association, and dissent.

d. Institute effective and efficient access to administrative and independent judicial procedures, including remedies and redress for environmental harm and the threat of such harm.

e. Eliminate corruption in all public and private institutions.

f. Strengthen local communities, enabling them to care for their environments, and assign environmental responsibilities to the levels of government where they can be carried out most effectively.

14. Integrate into formal education and life-long learning the knowledge, values, and skills needed for a sustainable way of life.

a. Provide all, especially children and youth, with educational opportunities that empower them to contribute actively to sustainable development.

b. Promote the contribution of the arts and humanities as well as the sciences in sustainability education.

c. Enhance the role of the mass media in raising awareness of ecological and social challenges.

d. Recognize the importance of moral and spiritual education for sustainable living.

15. Treat all living beings with respect and consideration.

a. Prevent cruelty to animals kept in human societies and protect them from suffering.

b. Protect wild animals from methods of hunting, trapping, and fishing that cause extreme, prolonged, or avoidable suffering.

c. Avoid or eliminate to the full extent possible the taking or destruction of non-targeted species.

16. Promote a culture of tolerance, nonviolence, and peace.

a. Encourage and support mutual understanding, solidarity, and cooperation among all peoples and within and among nations.

b. Implement comprehensive strategies to prevent violent conflict and use collaborative problem solving to manage and resolve environmental conflicts and other disputes.

c. Demilitarize national security systems to the level of a non-provocative defense posture, and convert military resources to peaceful purposes, including ecological restoration.

d. Eliminate nuclear, biological, and toxic weapons and other weapons of mass destruction.

e. Ensure that the use of orbital and outer space supports environmental protection and peace.

f. Recognize that peace is the wholeness created by right relationships with oneself, other persons, other cultures, other life, Earth, and the larger whole of which all are a part.

THE WAY FORWARD

As never before in history, common destiny beckons us to seek a new beginning. Such renewal is the promise of these Earth Charter principles. To fulfill this promise, we must commit ourselves to adopt and promote the values and objectives of the Charter.

This requires a change of mind and heart. It requires a new sense of global interdependence and universal responsibility. We must imaginatively develop and apply the vision of a sustainable way of life locally, nationally, regionally, and globally. Our cultural diversity is a precious heritage and different cultures will find their own distinctive ways to realize the vision. We must deepen and expand the global dialogue that generated the Earth Charter, for we have much to learn from the ongoing collaborative search for truth and wisdom.

Life often involves tensions between important values. This can mean difficult choices. However, we must find ways to harmonize diversity with unity, the exercise of freedom with the common good, short-term objectives with long-term goals. Every individual, family, organization, and community has a vital role to play. The arts, sciences, religions, educational institutions, media, businesses, nongovernmental organizations, and governments are all called to offer creative leadership. The partnership of government, civil society, and business is essential for effective governance.

In order to build a sustainable global community, the nations of the world must renew their commitment to the United Nations, fulfill their obligations under existing international agreements, and support the implementation of Earth Charter principles with an international legally binding instrument on environment and development.

Let ours be a time remembered for the awakening of a new reverence for life, the firm resolve to achieve sustainability, the quickening of the struggle for justice and peace, and the joyful celebration of life.

ORIGIN OF THE EARTH CHARTER

The Earth Charter was created by the independent Earth Charter Commission, which was convened as a follow-up to the 1992 Earth Summit in order to produce a global consensus statement of values and principles for a sustainable future. The document was developed over nearly a decade through an extensive process of international consultation, to which over five thousand people contributed. The Charter has been formally endorsed by thousands of organizations, including UNESCO and the IUCN (World Conservation Union). For more information, please visit www.EarthCharter.org.

The Problem of Sustainability

David W. Orr

If today is a typical day on planet earth, humans will add fifteen million tons of carbon to the atmosphere, destroy 115 square miles of tropical rainforest, create seventy-two square miles of desert, eliminate between forty to one hundred species, erode seventy-one million tons of topsoil, add twenty-seven hundred tons of CFCs to the stratosphere, and increase their population by 263,000. Yesterday, today, and tomorrow. By year's end the total numbers will be staggering: an area of tropical rainforest the size of the state of Kansas lost; seven to ten billion tons of carbon added to the atmosphere; a total population increase of ninety million. Looking further into the future, three crises are looming. The first is a food crisis evident in two curves that intersect in the not too distant future: one showing worldwide soil losses of twenty-four billion tons, the other a rapidly rising world population. The second crisis on the horizon is that caused by the end of the era of cheap energy. We are in a race between the exhaustion of fossil fuels, global warming, and the transition to a new era based on efficiency and solar energy. The third crisis, perhaps best symbolized by the looming prospect of a global climate change, has to do with ecological thresholds and the limits of natural systems. We can no longer assume that nature will be either bountiful or stable or that the earth will remain hospitable to civilization as we know it. These three crises feed upon each other. They are interactive in ways that we cannot fully anticipate. Together they constitute the first planetary crisis, one that will either spur humans to a much higher state or cause our demise. It is not too much to say that the decisions about how or whether life will be lived in the next century are being made now. We have a decade or two in which we must make unprecedented changes in the way we relate to each other and to nature.

In historical perspective, the crisis of sustainability appeared with unprecedented speed. Very little before the 1960s prepared us to understand the dynamics of complex, interactive systems and the force of exponential growth. A few prescient voices, including those of George Perkins Marsh, John Muir, Paul Sears, Fairfield Osborn, Aldo Leopold, William Vogt, and Rachel Carson, warned of resource shortages and the misuse of nature. But their warnings went largely unheard. Technological optimism, economic growth, and national power are deeply embedded in the modern psyche. The result is an enormous momentum in human affairs without as yet any good end in sight.

The crisis is unique in its range and scope including energy, resource use, climate, waste management, technology, cities, agriculture, water, biological resilience, international security, politics, and human values. Above all else it is a crisis of spirit and spiritual resources. We have it on high authority that without vision people perish. We need a new vision, a new story, as theologian Thomas Berry puts it, that links us to the planet in more life-centered ways. The causes of the crisis are related to those described by Marx, Weber, Durkheim, Dostoevsky, Freud, and Gandhi. But they dealt principally with the social effects of industrialization, not with its biophysical prospects. Even if these prospects were unclouded, we would have reason to question the human and societal effects of our present course. The anomie, rootlessness, and alienation of the modern world are part of a larger system of values, technologies, culture, and institutions which also produce acid rain, climate change, toxic wastes, terrorism, and nuclear bombs.

Differences exist whether these collectively represent a set of problems, which by definition are solvable with enough money, the right policies, and technology, or dilemmas for which there can be no purely technical solution. Put differently, can the values, institutions, and thrust of modern civilization be adapted to biophysical limits, or must we begin the task of consciously creating a postmodern world? These questions have to do with the causes of unsustainability. Where and how did we go wrong? What problems are we attempting to solve? How do these mesh with different policies, technologies, and behavior now proposed as solutions?

Five possibilities stand out. The crisis can be interpreted as a result of one or more social traps; it may stem from flaws in our understanding of the relation between the economy and the earth; it could be a result of the drive to dominate nature evident in our science and technology; it may have deeper roots that can be traced to wrong turns in our evolution; or finally, it may be due to sheer human perversity. I am inclined to believe that any full explanation of the causes of our plight would implicate all five. They are like the layers of an onion, peel one off and you discover yet another below. In the intellectual peeling, asking "why?" leads to the next layer and deeper levels of causation. I will consider these from the "outside in," from the most apparent and, I think, least problematic causes to deeper ones that become harder to define and more difficult to resolve.

THE CRISIS AS A SOCIAL TRAP

The crisis of sustainability is in part the result of rational behavior in "situation(s) characterized by multiple but conflicting rewards.... Social traps draw their victims into certain patterns of behavior with promises of immediate rewards and then confront them with consequences that the victims would rather avoid." Arms races, traffic jams, cigarette smoking, population explosions, and overconsumption are all traps in which individually rational behavior in the near term traps victims into long-term destructive outcomes. With each decision, players are lured into behavior that eventually undermines the health and stability of the system. In Garrett Hardin's essay "The Tragedy of the Commons," the villager rationally decides to graze an additional cow on an already overgrazed commons because the system rewards him for doing so. He can ignore the costs to others and eventually to himself, because payoffs reward irresponsibility. Similarly, in the name of national security, the Pentagon deploys a new weapon only to be matched or overmatched by others, which raises the costs of deadlock and increases the risks of ultimate catastrophe. In both cases the rewards are short-term (profit and prestige) and costs are long-term and paid by all.

To the extent that the crisis of sustainability is a product of social traps in the way we use fossil energy, land, water, forests, minerals, and biological diversity, the solutions must in one way or another change the timing of payoffs so that long-term costs are paid up front as part of the "purchase price." This is the rationale behind bottle bills and proposals for life-cycle or full costing. Hardin's villager would be deterred from grazing another cow by having to pay the full cost of additional damage to the commons. The Pentagon's weapons addiction might be reversed by something like a tax on all weapons that could be used offensively in direct proportion to their potential destructiveness. In these and other instances, honest bookkeeping would deter entry into social traps.

The theory is entirely plausible. No rational decisionmaker willingly pays higher costs for no net gain, and no rational society rewards members to undermine its existence. To the contrary, rational societies would reward decisions that lead to long-term collective benefits and punish the contrary. A sustainable society, then, will result from the calculus of self-interest. This approach requires minimal change in existing values, and fits most of our assumptions about human behavior derived from economics.

The theory is vulnerable, however, to some of the same criticisms made of market economics. Do we have, or can we acquire, full information about the long-term costs of our actions? In some important cases the answer is "No." Consumers who used freon-charged spray cans in the 1960s, thereby contributing to ozone depletion, could not be charged because no one knew the long-term costs involved. Given the dynamism of technology and the complexity of most human/environment interactions, it is not likely that many costs can be predicted in advance and assigned prices to effect decisions in a timely way. Some may not even be calculable in hindsight. But assuming complete information, would we willingly agree to pay full costs rather than defer costs to the future and/or to others? There is a peculiar recalcitrance in human affairs known to advertisers, theologians, and some historians. It has the common aspect of preference for self-aggrandizement in the short term, devil take the hindmost in the long term. People who choose to smoke or who refuse to wear seatbelts persist, not because they are rational, but because they can rationalize. Some who risk life and livelihood for others do so not because these represent "rational" choices, as that word is commonly understood, but because of some higher motivation (I remain unconvinced by arguments to the contrary made by sociobiologists).

Efforts to build a sustainable society on assumptions of human rationality must be regarded as partial solutions and first steps. Acknowledgement of social traps and designing policies to avoid them in the first place would, however, constitute important steps in building a sustainable society. Why we fall into social traps and generally find it difficult to acknowledge their existence—that is, to behave rationally—leads to the consideration of deeper causes.

THE CRISIS AS A CONSEQUENCE OF
ECONOMIC GROWTH

A second and related cause of the crisis of sustainability has to do with the propensity of all industrial societies to grow beyond the limits of natural systems. Economic growth is commonly regarded as the best measure of government performance. It has come to be the central mission of all developed and developing societies. In political scientist Henry Teune's words: "An individually based secular morality cannot accept a world without growth." (Since sooner or later we will have to accept such a world, perhaps Professor Teune has unwittingly sounded the death knell for an "individually based secular morality.") Growth, he asserts, is necessary for social order, economic efficiency, equitable distribution, environmental quality, and freedom of choice. In the course of his argument we are instructed that agribusiness is more efficient than family farms, which is not true, that forests are doing fine, which is not true, and that we are all beneficiaries of nuclear power, which deserves no comment. Nowhere does Teune acknowledge the dependence of the economy on the larger economy of nature, or the unavoidable limits set by that larger economy. For example, humans now use directly and indirectly forty percent of the net primary productivity of terrestrial ecosystems on the planet, thus changing climate, exterminating species, and toxifying ecosystems. How much more of nature can we coopt without undermining the biophysical basis of civilization, not to mention growth? Professor Teune does not say.

The most striking aspect of arguments for unending growth is the presumption that it is the normal state of things. Nothing could be further from the truth. The growth economy along with much of the modern world is, in a larger view, an aberration. For perspective, if we compare the evolutionary history of the planet to a week's time, as David Brower proposes, the industrial revolution occurred just 1/40th of a second before midnight on the seventh day, and the explosive economic growth since 1945 occurred in the last 1/500th of a second before midnight. In the words of historian Walter Prescott Webb, the years between 1500 and 1900 were "a boom such as the world had never known before and probably never can know again." The discovery of a "vast body of wealth without proprietors" in the new world radically altered ratios of resources to people. But by the time Frederick Jackson Turner announced the closing of the American frontier in 1893, these ratios were once again what they had been in the year 1500. Technology, for Webb, offered no way out: "On the broad flat plain of monotonous living [he was from Texas] we see the distorted images of our desires glimmering on the horizons of the future; we press on toward them only to have them disappear completely or reappear in a different form in another direction." Webb would not have been surprised either by the frantic expectations raised by the prospect of cold fusion, or by its rapid demise. For him, the inexorable facts were the ratios of people to land and resources.

Twenty-two years later, a team of systems scientists at MIT armed with computer models came to similar conclusions. Their results showed that population and resource use could not continue to grow exponentially without catastrophic collapse within a century. Marked increases in resource efficiency and pollution control did not appreciably alter the results. Catastrophe in exponentially growing systems is not necessarily evident until it is too late to avert.

The assumption of perpetual growth raises fundamental questions about the theoretical foundations of modern economics. Growth does not happen without cause. It is in large part the result of a body of ideas and theories that inform, motivate, and justify economic behavior. The world economy has expanded by thirteen hundred percent in the twentieth century. Can this expansion continue indefinitely? Mainstream economists are evidently still in agreement with conclusions reached by Harold Barnett and Chandler Morse in 1963:

> Advances in fundamental science have made it possible to take advantage of the uniformity of matter/energy—a uniformity that makes it feasible, without preassignable limit, to escape the quantitative constraints imposed by the character of the earth's crust.... Science, by making the resource base more homogeneous, erases the restrictions once thought to reside in the lack of homogeneity. In a neo-Ricardian world, it seems, the particular resources with which one starts increasingly become a matter of indifference. The reservation of particular resources for later use, therefore, may contribute little to the welfare of future generations.

Or as Harvard economist Robert Solow once said: "The world can, in effect, get along without natural resources." For Julian Simon, resources "are not finite in any economic sense." Human ingenuity is "the ultimate resource" (the title of Simon's book) and will enable us to overcome constraints that are merely biophysical.

Outside the mainstream, a postmodern economics is emerging. It begins with the fact that the economic process is governed by the laws of thermodynamics: "The economic process consists of a continuous transformation of low entropy into high entropy, that is, into irrevocable waste." The laws of thermodynamics (that is, we can neither create nor destroy energy and matter; and the process goes from ordered matter or "low entropy" to waste or "high entropy") set irrevocable limits to economic processes. We burn a lump of coal, low entropy, and create ashes and heat, high entropy. Faster economic growth only increases the rate at which we create high entropy in the form of waste, heat, garbage, and disorder. The destiny of the human species, according to Georgescu-Roegen, "is to choose a truly great, but brief, not a long and dull, career."

Economic growth is the sum total of what individual people do. And at the heart of conventional growth economics one meets a theoretical construct that economists have named "economic man," a proudly defiant moral disaster programmed to maximize his utility, which is whatever he is willing to pay for. By all accounts this includes a great many things and services that used to be freely included as a part of the fabric of life in societies with village greens, front porches, good neighbors, sympathetic saloon keepers, and competent people. Economic man knows no limits of discipline, or obligation, or satiation, which may explain why the growth economy has no logical stopping point, and perhaps why good neighbors are becoming harder to find. Psychologists identify this kind of behavior in humans as "infantile self-gratification." When this kind of behavior is manifested by entire societies, economists describe it as "mature capitalism."

In a notable book in 1977, economist Fred Hirsch described other limits to growth that were inherently social. As the economy grows, the goods and services available to everyone theoretically increase, except for those that are limited, like organizational directorships and lakeside homes, which Hirsch calls "positional goods." After basic biological and physical needs are met, an increasing portion of consumption is valued because it raises one's status in society. But, "If everyone in a crowd stands on tiptoe," as Hirsch puts it, "no one sees better." Rising levels of consumption do not necessarily increase one's status. Consumption of positional goods, however, gives some the power to stand on a ladder. The rest are not necessarily worse off physically, but are decidedly worse off psychologically. The attendant effects on economic psychology "become an increasing brake" on economic growth. Growing numbers of people whose appetites have been whetted by the promise of growth find only social congestion that limits leadership opportunities and status. As Hirsch puts it:

> The locus of instability is the divergence between what is possible for the individual and what is possible for all individuals. Increased material resources enlarge the demand for positional goods, a demand that can be satisfied for some only by frustrating demand by others.

The results, which he describes as the "economics of bad neighbors," include a decline in friendliness, the loss of altruism and mutual obligation, increased time pressures, and indifference to public welfare. Moreover, the pursuit of private and individual satisfaction by corporations and consumers undermines the very moral underpinnings—honesty, frugality, hard work, craftsmanship, and cooperation—necessary for the system to function. In short, after basic biological needs are met, further growth both "fails to deliver its full promise" and "undermines its social foundations."

The economist Joseph Schumpeter once made a similar argument. Capitalism, he thought, would ultimately undermine the noncapitalist attitudes and morale necessary to its stability. "There is in the capitalist system," he wrote in 1942, "a tendency for self-destruction." Robert Heilbroner argues similarly that business civilization will decline not only because of pollution and "obstacles of nature," but also because of the "erosion of the 'spirit' of capitalism." A business civilization inevitably becomes more "hollow" as material goods fail to satisfy deeper needs, including those for truth and meaningful work. Its demise will result from the "vitiation of the spirit that is sapping business civilization from within." At the very time that the system needs the loyalty of its participants most, they will be indifferent or hostile to it.

If the evidence suggest that economic growth is ecologically destructive, and soon to be constrained by biophysical and/or social limits, why do most economists want even more of it? A common answer is that growth is necessary to improve the situation of the poor. But this has not happened as promised. The rapid growth of the 1980s increased the concentration of wealth in the United States: the top one percent now control 34.3 percent of the wealth. The same pattern is evident worldwide, as the gap between the richest and poorest has widened from 3:1 in 1800 to 25:1 at present. Within poor countries, the benefits of growth go to the wealthiest, not to those who need them most. The importance of growth to the modern economy cannot be justified empirically on the grounds that it creates equity. Growth serves other functions, one of which is the avoidance of having to face the issue of fair distribution. As long as the total pie is growing, absolute but not relative wealth can be increased. If growth stops for any reason, the questions of distribution become acute. Political scientist Volkmar Lauber has made a good case that "the main motivation of growth...is not the pursuit of material gratification by the masses but the pursuit of power by elites." His case rests in part on analysis of public opinion polls in Europe and the United States showing only indifferent support for economic growth and much stronger support for quality of life improvements. In other words, economic growth occurs not because people demand it, but because elites do. Growth makes the wealthy more so, but it also gives substantial power to government and corporate elites who manage the economy, its technology, and all of its side effects.

From the perspective of physics and ecology, the flaws in mainstream economics are fundamental and numerous. First, the discipline lacks a concept of optimal size, which is a polite way of saying that it has confused bloatedness with prosperity. Second, it mistakenly regards an increasing gross national product as an achievement, rather than as a cost required to maintain a given level of population and artifacts. Third, it lacks an ecologically and morally defensible model of the "reasonable person," helping to create the behavior it purports only to describe. Fourth, growth economics has radically misconceived nature as a stock to be used up. The faster a growing volume of materials flows from mines, wells, forests farms, and oceans through the economic pipeline into dumps and sinks the better. Depletion at both ends of this stream explains what Wendell Berry calls the "ever-increasing hurry of research and exploration" driven by the "desperation that naturally and logically accompanies gluttony." Fifth, growth economics assumes that the human economy is independent of the larger economy of nature with its cycles and ecological interdependencies, and of the laws of physics that govern the flow of energy.

The prominence of the economy in the modern world, and that of growth economics in the conduct of public affairs explains, I think, a great deal of the propensity for social traps. The cultivation of mass consumption through advertising promotes the psychology of instant gratification and easy consumer credit, which create pressures that lead to risky technological fixes, perhaps the biggest trap of all. The discipline of economics has taught us little or nothing of the discipline imposed on us by physics and by natural systems. To the contrary, these are regarded as minor impediments to be overcome by substitution of materials and by the laws of supply and demand. But economics is, in turn, a part of a larger enterprise to dominate nature through science and technology.

THE CRISIS AS THE RESULT OF THE URGE
TO DOMINATE NATURE

At a deeper level, then, the crisis of sustainability can be traced to a drive to dominate nature that is evident in Western science and technology. But what is the source of that urge? One possibility, according to historian Lynn White, is that the drive to dominate nature is inherent in Judaic-Christian values. The writers of Genesis commanded us to be fruitful, multiply, and to have dominion over the earth and its creatures. We have done as instructed. And this, according to White, is the source of our problems. But the Bible says many things, some of which are ecologically sound. Even if it did not, there is a long time between the writing of Genesis and the onset of the problems of sustainability. An even larger gap may exist between biblical commandments generally and human behavior. We are enjoined, for example, to love our enemies, but as yet without comparable results. Something beyond faith seems to be at work. That something is perhaps found in more proximate causes: capitalism, the cult of instrumental reason, and industrial culture.

Lewis Mumford attributes the urge to dominate nature to the founders of modern science: Bacon, Galileo, Newton, and Descartes. Each, in Mumford's words, "lost sight of both the significance of nature and the nature of significance." Each contributed to the destruction of an organic world view and to the development of a mechanical world that traded the "totality of human experience...for that minute portion which can be observed within a limited time span and interpreted in terms of mass and motion."

Similar themes are found earlier in writings of Martin Heidigger and Alfred North Whitehead, and in the recent work of Carolyn Merchant, William Leiss, Morris Berman, Jacques Ellul, and nearly all critics of technology. With varying emphases, all argue that modern science has fundamentally misconceived the world by fragmenting reality, separating observer from observed, portraying the world as a mechanism, and dismissing nonobjective factors, all in the service of the domination of nature. The result is a radical miscarriage of human purposes and a distortion of reality under the guise of objectivity. Beneath the guise, however, lurks a crisis of rationality in which means are confused with ends and the domination of nature leads to the domination of other persons. In C. S. Lewis's words:

> At the moment, then, of man's victory over nature, we find the whole human race subjected to some individual men, and individuals subjected to that in themselves which is purely 'natural'—to their irrational impulses. Nature, untrammelled by values, rules the Conditioners and, through them, all humanity.

The crisis of rationality of which Lewis wrote is becoming acute with the advent of nuclear weapons and genetic engineering. In a remarkable article entitled "The Presumptions of Science" in the journal *Daedalus* in 1978, biologist Robert Sinsheimer asked: "Can there be forbidden or inopportune knowledge?" *Frankenstein* was Mary Shelley's way of asking a similar question one hundred sixty years earlier: Is there knowledge for which we are unwilling or unable to take responsibility? Thoroughly modern humans believe quite fervently that all knowledge is good and its embodiment in technology unproblematic. These articles of faith rest, as Sinsheimer notes, on the belief that "nature does not set traps for unwary species," and that our social institutions are sufficiently resilient to contain the political and economic results of continual technological change. He recommends that "we forgo certain technologies, even certain lines of inquiry where the likely application is incompatible with the maintenance of other freedoms."

The idea that science and technology should be limited on grounds of ecological prudence or morality apparently struck too close to the presumptions of establishment science for comfort. Sinsheimer's article was met with a thundering silence. Science and technology have become sanctified in Western culture. Research, adding to society's total inventory of undigested bits of knowledge, is now perhaps as holy a calling as saving the heathen was in other times. Yet the evidence mounts that unfettered scientific exploration, now mostly conducted in large, well-funded government or corporate laboratories, compounds the difficulties of building a sustainable society. Weapons labs create continual upward pressures on the arms race independent of political and policy considerations. The same is true in the economy where production technologies displace workers, threaten the economies of whole regions, and introduce a constant stream of environment-threatening changes (for example, ten thousand new chemicals introduced each year; synthetic fabrics substituted for cotton and wool; plastics for leather and cellulose; detergents for soap; chemical fertilizers for manure fossil; or nuclear energy for human, natural, or animal energy). In each case, the reason for the change has to do with economic pressures and technological opportunities. In historian Donald Worster's words, the problem posed by science and technology lies "in that complex and ambitious brain of Homo sapiens, in our unmatched capacity to experiment and explain, in our tendency to let reason outrun the constraints of love and stewardship..." For Worster, as for Sinsheimer, we need "the most stringent controls over research."

On the other side of the issue is the overwhelming majority of scientists, engineers, and their employers who regard science and technological innovation as inherently good and essential either to surmount natural constraints (the cornucopians) or to the development of energy and resource efficiency necessary for sustainability. These two positions differ not on the importance of knowledge, but over the kind of knowledge necessary. On the minority side are those seeking "old and solid knowledge," which used to be called wisdom. It has less to do with specialized learning and the cleverness of means than with broad, integrative understanding and the careful selection of ends. Such knowledge, in Wendell Berry's phrase, "solves for

pattern." It does not result, for example, in the expenditure of millions of federal research dollars to develop genetically derived ways to increase milk production at the same time that the U.S. Department of Agriculture is spending millions to slaughter dairy herds because of a milk glut.

No one, of course, is against wisdom. But while we mass-produce technological cleverness in research universities, we assume that wisdom can take care of itself. The results of technical research are evident and most often profitable. Wisdom is not so easy—what passes for wisdom may be only eloquent foolishness. Real wisdom may not be particularly useful. The search for integrative knowledge would probably not contribute much to the gross national product, or to the list of our technological achievements, and certainly not to our capacity to destroy. As often as not, it might lead us to stop doing a lot of things that we are now doing, and to reflect more on what we ought to do.

But for those who advocate controls on scientific inquiry and technology, three major problems arise. The first is that of separating the baby from the bathwater. Research needs to be done, and appropriate technologies will be important building blocks of a sustainable world. In this category, I would include research into energy efficiency and solar technologies, materials efficiency, the restoration of damaged ecosystems, the knowledge of how to build healthy cities and to revitalize rural areas, how to grow food in an environmentally sound manner, and research on the conditions of peace. These are things on which our survival, health, peace, and peace of mind depend. Without much effort, we could assemble another list of research that works in the opposite direction. The challenge before us is to learn how to make distinctions between knowledge that we need from that which we do not need, including that which we cannot control. This distinction will not always be clear in advance, nor can it be enforced at all times. What is possible, however, is to clarify the relationship between technology, knowledge, and the goals of sustainability, and to use that knowledge to shift public R and D expenditures accordingly.

A second problem is the real possibility that controls will undermine freedom of inquiry and first-amendment guarantees. Sinsheimer argues that freedom of inquiry be balanced against other freedoms and values. Freedom of inquiry, in short, is not an absolute, but must be weighed against other values, including the safety and survival of the system that makes inquiry possible in the first place. A third concern is the effectiveness of any system of controls. Sinsheimer proposes that limits be placed on funding and access to instruments, while admitting that past efforts to control science have given license to bigots and charlatans. Part of the difficulty lies in our inability to predict the consequences of research and technological change. Most early research is probably innocent enough, and becomes dangerous only later when converted into weapons, reactors, PCBs, and production systems. Even these cannot automatically be regarded as bad without reference to their larger social, political, economic, and ecological context. If one society successfully limits potentially dangerous scientific inquiry, however, work by scientists elsewhere continues unless similarly proscribed. The logic of the system of research and technological development operates by the same dynamics evident in arms races or Hardin's tragedy of the commons. Failure to pursue technological developments, regardless of their side effects, places a corporation or government at a potential disadvantage in a system where competitiveness and survival are believed to be synonymous.

There are no easy answers to issues posed by technology and science, but there is no escape from their consequences. At every turn the prospects for sustainability hinge on the resolution of problems and dilemmas posed by that double-edged sword of unfettered human ingenuity. At the point where we choose to confront the effects of science and technology, we will discover no adequate philosophy of technology to light our path. Technology has expanded so rapidly and initially with so much promise that few thought to ask elementary questions about its relation to human purposes and prospects. Intoxication replaced prudence.

There is another way to see the problem. Perhaps much of our technology is not taking us where we want to go anyway. The thrust of technology has almost always been to make the world more effortless and efficient. The logical end of technological progress, as George Orwell once put it, was to "reduce the human being to something resembling a brain in a bottle...to make the world safe for little fat men." Our goal, Orwell thought, should be to "make life simpler and harder instead of softer and more complex." Making life simpler, ecologically sustainable, more friendly, and more conducive to human growth requires only a fraction of the technology now available.

Technological extravagance is most often justified because it makes our economy more competitive, that is, it enables us to grow faster than other economies. In doing so, however, we find ourselves locked into behavior patterns that impose long-term costs for short-term gains. Beyond social traps, growth economics, and the drive to dominate nature are more distant causes having to do with human evolution and the human condition.

THE CRISIS AS THE RESULT OF AN EVOLUTIONARY WRONG TURN

Perhaps in the transition from hunter-gatherer societies to agricultural and urban cultures we took the wrong fork in the road. That primitive hunter-gatherer societies more often than not lived in some stable harmony with the natural world is of some embarrassment to the defenders of the faith in progress, as is the fact that they did so at a high quality of life, with ample leisure time for cultural pursuits and with high levels of equality. The designation of hunter-gatherers as "primitive" is a useful rationalization for cultural, political, and economic domination. In spite of vast evidence to the contrary, we insist that Western civilization should be the model for everyone else, but for most anthropologists there is no such thing as a superior culture, hence none that can rightly be labeled as primitive. Colin Turnbull concluded in *The Human Cycle* that in many respects hunter-gatherer tribes handled various life stages better than contemporary societies. In Stanley Diamond's words, the reason "springs from the very center of civilization, not from too much knowledge but from too little wisdom. What primitives possess—the immediate and ramifying sense of the person, and...an existential humanity—we have largely lost."

If civilization represents a mistaken evolutionary path, what can we do? Paul Shepard proposes a radical program of cultural restructuring that would combine elements of hunter-gatherer cultures with high technology and the wholesale redesign of contemporary civilization. Recently, he has proposed a more modest course that requires rethinking the conduct of childhood and the need to connect the psyche with the earth in the earliest years. Contact with earth, soil, wildlife, trees, and animals, he believes, is the substrate that orients adult thought and behavior to life. Without this contact with nature, maturity is spurious, resulting in "childish adults" with "the world's flimsiest identity structures."

For all of the difficulty in translating the work of Sahlins, Diamond, Shepard, and others into a coherent strategy for change, they offer three perspectives important for thinking about sustainability. First, from their work we know more about the range of possible human institutions and economies. In many respects, the modern world suffers by comparison with earlier cultures from a lack of complexity, if not complicatedness. This is not to argue for a simple-minded return to some mythical Eden, but an acknowledgment that earlier cultures were not entirely unsuccessful in wrestling with the problems of life, nor we entirely successful. Second, from their work, we know that aggressiveness, greed, violence, sexism, and alienation are in large part cultural artifacts not inherent in the human psyche. Earlier cultures did not engender these traits nearly as much as mass-industrial societies have. Riane Eisler, in reinterpreting much of the prehistorical record, concludes that the norm prior to the year 5000 was peaceful societies that were neither matriarchal nor patriarchal. Third, the study of other cultures offers a tantalizing glimpse of how culture can be linked to nature through ritual, myth, and social organization. Our alienation from the natural world is unprecedented. Healing this division is a large part of the difference between survival and extinction. If difficult to embody in a programmatic way, anthropology suggests something of lost possibilities and future potentials. A fifth possibility remains to be considered having to do with the wellsprings of human behavior.

THE CRISIS OF SUSTAINABILITY AND THE HUMAN CONDITION

In considering the causes of the crisis of sustainability, there is a tendency to sidestep the possibility that we are a flawed, cantankerous, willful, perhaps fallen, but certainly not entirely planet-broken, race. These traits, however, may explain evolutionary wrong turns, flaws in our culture and science, and an affinity for social traps. It's us. Philosophers call this the 'human condition'. In Ernest Becker's words: "We are doomed to live in an overwhelmingly tragic and demonic world." The demonic is found in our insatiable restlessness, greed, passions, and urge to dominate whether fueled by eros, thanatos, fear of death, or the echoes of our ancient reptilian brain. At the collective level, there may be what John Livingston calls "species ambition" that stems from our chronic insecurity. "The harder we struggle toward immortality," he writes, "the fiercer becomes the suffocating vise of alienation." We are caught between the drive for Promethean immortality, which takes us to extinction, and what appears to be a meaningless survival in the recognition that we are only a part of a larger web of life. Caught between the prospect of a brief, exciting career and a long, dull one, the anxious animal chooses the former. In this statement of the problem we can recognize a variant of Bateson's double bind from which there is no purely logical escape.

Can we build a sustainable society without seeking first the Kingdom of God or some reasonable facsimile thereof? Put differently, is cleverness enough, or will we have to be good in both the moral and ecological sense of the word? And if so, what does goodness mean in

an ecological perspective? The best answer to this question I believe was given by Aldo Leopold: "A thing is right when it tends to preserve the integrity, stability, and beauty of the biotic community. It is wrong when it tends otherwise." The essence of Leopold's Land Ethic is "respect for his fellow members, and also respect for the (biotic) community as such." Respect implies a sense of limits, things one does not do, not because they cannot be done but because they should not be done. But the idea of limits, or even community, runs counter to the Promethean mentality of technological civilization and the individualism of *laissez faire* economics. At the heart of both, David Ehrenfeld argues, is an overblown faith in our ability "to rearrange the world of nature and the affairs of men and women." But "In no important instance," he writes, "have we been able to demonstrate comprehensive successful management of our world, nor do we understand it well enough to be able to manage it in theory." Even if we could do so, we could never outrun all of the ghosts and fears that haunt Promethean men.

All theological explanations, then, lead to proposals for a change in consciousness and deeper self-knowledge that recognize the limits of human rationality. In Carl Jung's words: "We cannot and ought not to repudiate reason, but equally we must cling to the hope that instinct will hasten to our aid." The importance of theological perspectives in the dialogue about sustainability lies in their explicit recognition of persistent and otherwise inexplicable tragedy and suffering in history, and in history to come—even in a world that is otherwise sustainable. This realism can provide deeper insight into human motives and potentials, and an antidote to giddy and breathless talk of new ages and paradigm shifts. Whatever a sustainable society may be, it must be built on the most realistic view of the human condition possible. Whatever the perspectives of its founders, it must be resilient enough to tolerate the stresses of human recalcitrance. Theological perspectives may also alert us to the physics of goodness in the certainty that a sustainable society will require a great deal of it. They also alert us to the desirability of scratching where we itch. If we can fulfill all of our consumer needs, desires, and fantasies, as cornucopians like Julian Simon or devotees of technology and efficiency predict, there may be other nightmares ahead of the sort envisioned by Huxley in *Brave New World* or that which afflicted King Midas. There is good reason not to get everything we want, and some reason to believe that in the act of consumption and fantasy fulfillment we are scratching in the wrong place. But it is difficult to link these insights into a program for change, indeed the two may be antithetical. Jung, for one, dismissed the hyperintellectuality found in most rational schemes in favor of the process of metanoia arising from the collective unconscious. After a lifetime of reflection on these problems, Lewis Mumford could only propose grass-roots efforts toward a decentralized, "organic" society based on "biotechnics," and "something like a spontaneous religious conversion...that will replace the mechanical world picture with an organic world picture."

CONCLUSION: CAUSATION IN HISTORICAL PERSPECTIVE

The crisis of sustainability is without precedent, as is the concept of a sustainable society. In attempting to build a durable social order we must acknowledge that efforts to change society for the better have a dismal history. Societies change continually, but seldom in directions hoped for, for reasons that we fully understand, and with consequences that are anticipated. Nor, to my knowledge, has any society planned and successfully moved toward greater sustainability on a willing basis. To the contrary, the historical pattern is, in Chateaubriand's words, for "forests to precede civilization, deserts to follow." The normal response to crises of carrying capacity has not been to develop a carefully calibrated response meshing environmental demands with what the ecosystem can sustain over the long run. Rather, the record reveals either the collapse of the offending culture, or technological adaptation that opens new land (new sources of carbon), water, or energy (including slave labor to contemporary use of fossil fuels). Economic development has largely been a crisis-driven process that occurs when a society outgrows its resource base.

The argument, then, that humankind has always triumphed over adversity in the past, and will therefore automatically meet the challenges of the future, has the distinction of being at once bad history and irrelevant. Optimists of the "ultimate resource" genre neglect the fact that history is a tale written by the winners. The losers, including those who violated the commandments of carrying capacity, disappeared mostly without writing much. We know of their demise in part through painstaking archeological reconstruction that reveals telltale signs of overpopulation, desertification, deforestation, famine, and social breakdown—what ecologists call "overshoot."

Even if humankind had always triumphed over challenges, the present crisis of sustainability is qualitatively different, without any historical precedent. It is the first truly global crisis. It is also unprecedented in its sheer complexity. Whether by economics, policy, passion, edu-

cation, moral suasion, or some combination of the above, advocates of sustainability propose to remake the human role in nature, substantially altering much that we have come to take for granted from Galileo and Adam Smith to the present. Most advocates of sustainability recognize that it will also require sweeping changes in the relations between people, societies, and generations. And all of these must, by definition, have a high degree of permanence. In their range, number, and urgency, these are not modest goals.

Still, history may provide important parallels and perspectives, beginning with the humbling awareness that we live on a planet littered with ruins that testify to the fallibility of our past judgments and foresight. Human folly will undoubtedly accompany us on the journey toward sustainability, which further suggests something about how that journey should be made. This will be a long journey. The poet Gary Snyder writes of a thousand-year process. Economists frequently write as if several decades will do. Between the poet's millennia and the economist's decades, I think it is reasonable to expect a transition of several centuries. But the major actions to stabilize the vital signs of earth and stop the hemorrhaging of life must be made within the next decade or two.

History, however, gives many examples of change that did not occur, and of other changes that were perverted. The Enlightenment faith in reason to solve human problems ended in the bloody excesses of the French Revolution. In historian Peter Gay's words:

> The world has not turned out the way the philosophes wished and half expected that it would. Old fanaticisms have been more intractable, irrational forces more inventive than the philosophes were ready to conjecture in their darkest moments. Problems of race, of class, of nationalism, of boredom and despair in the midst of plenty have emerged almost in defiance of the philosophes' philosophy. We have known horrors, and may know horrors, that the men of the Enlightenment did not see in their nightmares.

To the extent that the faith in reason survives, it is applied to narrow issues of technology. The difference, in Leo Marx's words, "turns on the apparent loss of interest in, or unwillingness to name, the social ends for which the scientific and technological instruments of power are to be used." Similarly, Karl Marx's vision of a humane society became the nightmare of Stalin's Gulags.

In our own history, progressive reforms far more modest than those necessary for sustainability have run aground on the shoals of corporate politics. The high democratic ideals of late nineteenth-century populism gave way to a less noble reality. In one historian's words:

A consensus thus came to be silently ratified: reform politics need not concern itself with structural alteration of the economic customs of the society. This conclusion , of course, had the effect of removing from mainstream reform politics the idea of people in an industrial society gaining significant degrees of autonomy in the structure of their own lives.... Rather,...the citizenry is persuaded to accept the system as 'democratic'—even as the private lives of millions become more deferential, anxiety-ridden, and less free.

A similar process is apparent in the decline of the reforms of the 1960s, which began with the high hopes of building "participatory democracy" described in the Port Huron Statement, only to tragically fall apart in chaos, camp, racism, assassinations, domestic violence, FBI surveillance, and a war that never should have been fought.

History is a record of many things, most of which were not planned or foreseen. And in the same century as Auschwitz, Hiroshima, and the H-bomb, we know that at best it is only partially a record of progress. It is easy at this point to throw up one's hands and conclude with the Kentucky farmer who informed the lost traveler that "you can't get there from here." That conclusion, however, breeds self-fulfilling prophecies, fatalism, and resignation—perhaps in the face of opportunities, but certainly in the face of an overwhelming need to act. We also have the historical examples of Gandhi, Martin Luther King, and Alfred Schweitzer suggesting a different social dynamic, one that places less emphasis on confrontation, revolution, and slogans, and more on patience, courage, moral energy, humility, and nonpolarizing means of struggle. And we have the wisdom of E. F. Schumacher's admonition to avoid asking whether we will succeed or not and instead to "leave these perplexities behind us and get down to work."

Finally, the word 'crisis', based on a medical analogy, misleads us into thinking that after the fever breaks things will revert to normal. This is not so. As long as anything like our present civilization lasts it must monitor and restrain human demands against the biosphere. This will require an unprecedented vigilance and the institutionalization (or ritualization) of restraints through some combination of law, coercion, education, religion, social structure, myth, taboo, and market forces. History offers little help, since there is no example of a society that was or is both technologically dynamic and environmentally sustainable. It remains to be seen how and whether these two can be harmonized.

Ecological Literacy

David W. Orr

Literacy is the ability to read. Numeracy is the ability to count. Ecological literacy, according to Garrett Hardin, is the ability to ask "What then?" Considerable attention is properly being given to our shortcomings in teaching the young to read, count, and compute, but not nearly enough to ecological literacy. Reading, after all, is an ancient skill. And for most of the twentieth century we have been busy adding, subtracting, multiplying, dividing, and now computing. But "What then?" questions have not come easy for us despite all of our formidable advances in other areas. Napoleon did not ask the question, I gather, until he had reached the outskirts of Moscow, by which time no one could give a good answer except "Let's go back home." If Custer asked the question, we have no record of it. His last known words at Little Big Horn were, "Hurrah, boys, now we have them," a stirring if dubious pronouncement. And economists, who are certainly both numerate and numerous, have not asked the question often enough. Asking "What then?" on the west side of the Niemen River, or at Fort Laramie, would have saved a lot of trouble. For the same reason, "What then?" is also an appropriate question to ask before the last rain forests disappear, before the growth economy consumes itself into oblivion, and before we have warmed the planet intolerably.

The failure to develop ecological literacy is a sin of omission and of commission. Not only are we failing to teach the basics about the earth and how it works, but we are in fact teaching a large amount of stuff that is simply wrong. By failing to include ecological perspectives in any number of subjects, students are taught that ecology is unimportant for history, politics, economics, society, and so forth. And through television they learn that the earth is theirs for the taking. The result is a generation of ecological yahoos without a clue why the color of the water in their rivers is related to their food supply, or why storms are becoming more severe as the planet warms. The same persons as adults will create businesses, vote, have families, and above all, consume. If they come to reflect on the discrepancy between the splendor of their private lives in a hotter, more toxic and violent world, as ecological illiterates they will have roughly the same success as one trying to balance a checkbook without knowing arithematic.

FORMATION OF ATTITUDES

To become ecologically literate one must certainly be able to read and, I think, even like to read. Ecological literacy also presumes an ability to use numbers, and the ability to know what is countable and what is not, which is to say the limits of numbers. But these are indoor skills. Ecological literacy also requires the more demanding capacity to observe nature with insight, a merger of landscape and mindscape. "The interior landscape," in Barry Lopez's words, "responds to the character and subtlety of an exterior landscape; the shape of the individual mind is affected by land as it is by genes." The quality of thought is related to the ability to relate to "where on this earth one goes, what one touches, the patterns one observes in nature—the intricate history of one's life in the land, even a life in the city, where wind, the chirp of birds, the line of a falling leaf, are known." The fact that this kind of intimate knowledge of our landscapes is rapidly disappearing can only impoverish our mental landscapes as well. People who do not know the ground on which they stand miss one of the elements of good thinking which is the capacity to distinguish between health and disease in natural systems and their relation to health and disease in human ones.

If literacy is driven by the search for knowledge, ecological literacy is driven by the sense of wonder, the sheer delight in being alive in a beautiful, mysterious, bountiful world. The darkness and disorder that we have brought to that world give ecological literacy an urgency it lacked a century ago. We can now look over the abyss and see the end of it all. Ecological literacy begins in childhood. "To keep alive his inborn sense of wonder," a child, in Rachel Carson's words, "needs the companionship of at least one adult who can share it, rediscovering with him the joy, excitement and mystery of the world we live in." The sense of wonder is rooted in the emotions or what E. O. Wilson has called "biophilia," which is simply the affinity for the living world. The nourishment of that affinity is the beginning point for the sense of kinship with life, without which literacy of any sort will not help much. This is to say that even a thorough knowledge of the facts of life and of the threats to it will not save us in the absence of the feeling of kinship with life of the sort that cannot entirely be put into words.

There are, I think, several reasons why ecological literacy has been so difficult for Western culture. First, it implies the ability to think broadly, to know something of what is hitched to what. This ability is being lost in an age of specialization. Scientists of the quality of Rachel Carson or Aldo Leopold are rarities who must buck the pressures toward narrowness and also endure a great deal of professional rejection and hostility. By inquiring into the relationship between chlorinated hydrocarbon pesticides and bird populations, Rachel Carson was asking an ecolate question. Many others failed to ask, not because they did not like birds, but because they had not, for whatever reasons, thought beyond the conventional categories. To do so would have required that they relate their food system to the decline in the number of birds in their neighborhood. This means that they would have had some direct knowledge of farms and farming practices, as well as a comprehension of ornithology. To think in ecolate fashion presumes a breadth of experience with healthy natural systems, both of which are increasingly rare. It also presumes that the persons be willing and able to "think at right angles" to their particular specializations, as Leopold put it.

Ecological literacy is difficult, second, because we have come to believe that education is solely an indoor activity. A good part of it, of necessity, must be, but there is a price. William Morton Wheeler once compared the naturalist with the professional biologist in these words: "[The naturalist] is primarily an observer and fond of outdoor life, a collector, a classifier, a describer, deeply impressed by the overwhelming intricacy of natural phenomena and revelling in their very complexity." The biologist, on the other hand, "is oriented toward and dominated by ideas, and rather terrified or oppressed by the intricate hurly-burly of concrete, sensuous reality.... he is a denizen of the laboratory. His besetting sin is oversimplification and the tendency to undue isolation of the organisms he studies from their natural environment." Since Wheeler wrote, ecology has become increasingly specialized and, on suspects, remote from its subject matter. Ecology, like most learning worthy of the effort, is an applied subject. Its goal is not just a comprehension of how the world works, but, in the light of that knowledge, life lived accordingly. The same is true of theology, sociology, political science, and most other subjects that grace the conventional curriculum.

The decline in the capacity for aesthetic appreciation is a third factor working against ecological literacy. We have become comfortable

with all kinds of ugliness and seem incapable of effective protest against its purveyors: urban developers, businessmen, government officials, television executives, timber and mining companies, utilities, and advertisers. Rene Dubos once stated that our greatest disservice to our children was to give them the belief that ugliness was somehow normal. But disordered landscapes are not just an aesthetic problem. Ugliness signifies a more fundamental disharmony between people and between people and the land. Ugliness is, I think, the surest sign of disease, or what is now being called "unsustainability." Show me the hamburger stands, neon ticky-tacky strips leading toward every city in America, and the shopping malls, and I'll show you devastated rain forests, a decaying countryside, a politically dependent population, and toxic waste dumps. It is all of a fabric.

And this is the heart of the matter. To see things in their wholeness is politically threatening. To understand that our manner of living, so comfortable for some, is linked to cancer rates in migrant laborers in California, the disappearance of tropical rain forests, fifty thousand toxic dumps across the U.S.A., and the depletion of the ozone layer is to see the need for a change in our way of life. To see things whole is to see both the wounds we have inflicted on the natural world in the name of mastery and those we have inflicted on ourselves and on our children for no good reason, whatever our stated intentions. Real ecological literacy is radicalizing in that it forces us to reckon with the roots of our ailments, not just with their symptoms. For this reason, I think it leads to a revitalization and broadening of the concept of citizenship to include membership in a planetwide community of humans and living things.

And how does this striving for community come into being? I doubt that there is a single path, but there are certain common elements. First, in the lives of most if not all people who define themselves as environmentalists, there is experience in the natural world at an early age. Leopold came to know birds and wildlife in the marshes and fields around his home in Burlington, Iowa before his teens. David Brower, as a young boy on long walks over the Berkeley hills, learned to describe the flora to his nearly blind mother. Second, and not surprisingly, there is often an older teacher or mentor as a role model: a grandfather, a neighbor, an older brother, a parent, or teacher. Third, there are seminal books that explain, heighten, and say what we have felt deeply, but not said so well. In my own life, Rene Dubos and Loren Eiseley served this function of helping to bring feelings to articulate consciousness.

Ecological literacy is becoming more difficult, I believe, not because there are fewer books about nature, but because there is less opportunity for the direct experience of it. Fewer people grow up on farms or in rural areas where access is easy and where it is easy to learn a degree of competence and self-confidence toward the natural world. Where the ratio between the human-created environment to the purely natural world exceeds some point, the sense of place can only be a sense of habitat. One finds the habitat familiar and/or likeable but without any real sense of belonging in the natural world. A sense of place requires more direct contact with the natural aspects of a place, with soils, landscape, and wildlife. This sense is lost as we move down the continuum toward the totalized urban environment where nature exists in tiny, isolated fragments by permission only. Said differently, this is an argument for more urban parks, summer camps, green belts, wilderness areas, public seashores. If we must live in an increasingly urban world, let's make it one of well-designed compact green cities that include trees, river parks, meandering greenbelts, and urban farms where people can see, touch, and experience nature in a variety of ways. In fact, no other cities will be sustainable in a greenhouse world.

ECOLOGICAL LITERACY AND
FORMAL EDUCATION

The goal of ecological literacy as I have described it has striking implications for that part of education that must occur in classrooms, libraries, and laboratories. To the extent that most educators have noticed the environment, they have regarded it as a set of problems which are: (1) solvable (unlike dilemmas, which are not) by (2) the analytic tools and methods of reductionist science which (3) create value-neutral, technological remedies that will not create even worse side effects. Solutions, therefore, originate at the top of society, from governments and corporations, and are passed down to a passive citizenry in the form of laws, policies, and technologies. The results, it is assumed, will be socially, ethically, politically, and humanly desirable, and the will to live and to sustain a humane culture can be preserved in a technocratic society. In other words, business can go on as usual. Since there is no particular need for an ecologically literate and ecologically competent public, environmental education is most often regarded as an extra in the curriculum, not as a core requirement or as an aspect pervading the entire educational process.

Clearly, some parts of the crisis can be accurately described as problems. Some of these can be solved by technology, particularly

those that require increased resource efficiency. It is a mistake, however, to think that all we need is better technology, not an ecologically literate and caring public willing to help reduce the scale of problems by reducing its demands on the environment and to accept (even demand) public policies that require sacrifices. It all comes down to whether the public understands the relation between its well-being and the health of the natural systems.

For this to occur, we must rethink both the substance and the process of education at all levels. What does it mean to educate people to live sustainably, going, in Aldo Leopold's words, from "conqueror of the land community to plain member and citizen of it"? However it is applied in practice, the answer will rest on six foundations.

The first is the recognition that *all education is environmental education*. By what is included or excluded, emphasized or ignored, students learn that they are a part of or apart from the natural world. Through all education we inculcate the ideas of careful stewardship or carelessness. Conventional education, by and large, has been a celebration of all that is human to the exclusion of our dependence on nature. As a result, students frequently resemble what Wendell Berry has called "itinerant professional vandals," persons devoid of any sense of place or stewardship, or inkling of why these are important.

Second, *environmental issues are complex and cannot be understood through a single discipline or department*. Despite a decade or more of discussion and experimentation, interdisciplinary education remains an unfulfilled promise. The failure occurred, I submit, because it was tried within discipline-centric institutions. A more promising approach is to reshape institutions to function as transdisciplinary laboratories that include components such as agriculture, solar technologies, forestry, land management, wildlife, waste cycling, architectural design, and economics. Part of the task, then, of Earth-centered education is the study of interactions across the boundaries of conventional knowledge and experience.

Third, *for inhabitants, education occurs in part as a dialogue with a place and has the characteristics of good conversation*. Formal education happens mostly as a monologue of human interest, desires, and accomplishments that drowns out all other sounds. It is the logical outcome of the belief that we are alone in a dead world of inanimate matter, energy flows, and biogeochemical cycles. But true conversation can occur only if we acknowledge the existence and interests of the other. In conversation, we define ourselves, but in relation to another. The quality of conversation does not rest on the brilliance of one or the other person. It is more like a dance in which the artistry is mutual.

In good conversation, words represent reality faithfully. And words have power. They can enliven or deaden, elevate or degrade, but they are never neutral, because they affect our perception and ultimately our behavior. The use of words such as "resources," "manage," "channelize," "engineer," and "produce" makes our relation to nature a monologue rather than a conversation. The language of nature includes the sounds of animals, whales, birds, insects, wind, and water—a language more ancient and basic than human speech. Its books are the etchings of life on the face of the land. To hear this language requires patient, disciplined study of the natural world. But it is a language for which we have an affinity.

Good conversation is unhurried. It has its own rhythm and pace. Dialogue with nature cannot be rushed. It will be governed by cycles of day and night, the seasons, the pace of procreation, and by the larger rhythm of evolutionary and geologic time. Human sense of time is increasingly frenetic, driven by clocks, computers, and revolutions in transportation and communication.

Good conversation has form, structure, and purpose. Conversation with nature has the purpose of establishing, in Wendell Berry's words: "What is here? What will nature permit here? What will nature help us do here?" The form and structure of any conversation with the natural world is that of the discipline of ecology as a restorative process and healing art.

Fourth, it follows that *the way education occurs is as important as its content.* Students taught environmental awareness in a setting that does not alter their relationship to basic life-support systems learn that it is sufficient to intellectualize, emote, or posture about such things without having to live differently. Environmental education ought to change the way people live, not just how they talk. This understanding of education is drawn from the writings of John Dewey, Alfred North Whitehead, J. Glenn Gray, Paulo Friere, Ivan Illich, and Eliot Wigginton. Learning in this view best occurs in response to real needs and the life situation of the learner. The radical distinctions typically drawn between teacher and student, between the school and the community, and those between areas of knowledge, are dissolved. Real learning is participatory and experiential, not just didactic. The flow can be two ways between teachers, who best function as facilitators, and students who are expected to be active agents in defining what is learned and how.

Fifth, *experience in the natural world is both an essential part of understanding the environment, and conducive to good thinking.* Experience, properly conceived, trains the intellect to observe the land carefully and to distinguish between health and its opposite. Direct experience is an antidote to indoor, abstract learning. It is also a wellspring of good thinking. Understanding nature demands a disciplined and observant intellect. But nature, in Emerson's words, is also "the vehicle of thought" as a source of language, metaphor, and symbol. Natural diversity may well be the source of much of human creativity and intelligence. If so, the simplification and homogenization of ecosystems can only result in a lowering of human intelligence.

Sixth, *education relevant to the challenge of building a sustainable society will enhance the learner's competence with natural systems.* For reasons once explained by Whitehead and Dewey, practical competence is an indispensable source of good thinking. Good thinking proceeds from the friction between reflective thought and real problems. Aside from its effects on thinking, practical competence will be essential if sustainability requires, as I think it does, that people must take an active part in rebuilding their homes, businesses, neighborhoods, communities, and towns. Shortening supply lines for food, energy, water, and materials—while recycling waste locally—implies a high degree of competence not necessary in a society dependent on central vendors and experts.

THE AIM: ECOLOGICAL LITERACY

If these can be taken as the foundations of Earth-centered education, what can be said of its larger purpose? In a phrase, it is that quality of mind that seeks out connections. It is the opposite of the specialization and narrowness characteristic of most education. The ecologically literate person has the knowledge necessary to comprehend interrelatedness, and an attitude of care or stewardship. Such a person would also have the practical competence required to act on the basis of knowledge and feeling. Competence can only be derived from the experience of doing and the mastery of what Alasdair MacIntyre describes as a "practice." Knowing, caring, and practical competence constitute the basis of ecological literacy.

Ecological literacy, further, implies a broad understanding of how people and societies relate to each other and to natural systems, and how they might do so sustainably. It presumes both an awareness of the interrelatedness of life and knowledge of how the world works as a physical system. To ask, let alone answer, "What then?" questions presumes an understanding of concepts such as carrying capacity, overshoot, Liebig's Law of the minimum, thermodynamics, trophic levels, energetics, and succession. Ecological literacy presumes that we understand our place in the story of evolution. It is to know that our health, well-being, and ultimately our survival depend on working with, not against, natural forces. The basis for ecological literacy, then, is the comprehension of the interrelatedness of life grounded in the study of natural history, ecology, and thermodynamics. It is to understand that: "There ain't no such thing as a free lunch"; "You can never throw anything away"; and "The first law of intelligent tinkering is to keep all of the pieces." It is also to understand, with Leopold, that we live in a world of wounds senselessly inflicted on nature and on ourselves.

A second stage in ecological literacy is to know something of the speed of the crisis that is upon us. It is to know magnitudes, rates, and trends of population growth, species extinction, soil loss, deforestation, desertification, climate change, ozone depletion, resource exhaustion, air and water pollution, toxic and radioactive contamination, resource and energy use—in short, the vital signs of the planet and its ecosystems. Becoming ecologically literate is to understand the human enterprise for what it is: a sudden eruption in the enormity of evolutionary time.

Ecological literacy requires a comprehension of the dynamics of the modern world. The best starting place is to read the original rationale for the domination of nature found in the writings of Bacon, Descartes, and Galileo. Here one finds the justification for the union of science with power and the case for separating ourselves from nature in order to control it more fully. To comprehend the idea of controlling nature, one must fathom the sources of the urge to power and the paradox of rational means harnessed to insane ends portrayed in Marlowe's *Doctor Faustus*, Mary Shelley's *Frankenstein*, Melville's *Moby-Dick*, and Dostoevsky's "Legend of the Grand Inquisitor."

Ecological literacy, then, requires a thorough understanding of the ways in which people and whole societies have become destructive. The ecologically literate person will appreciate something of how social structures, religion, science, politics, technology, patriarchy, culture, agriculture, and human cussedness combine as causes of our predicament.

The diagnosis of the causes of our plight is only half of the issue. But before we can address solutions there are several issues that demand clarification. "Nature," for example, is variously portrayed as "red in tooth and claw," or, like the film "Bambi," full of sweet little critters. Economists see nature as natural resources to be used; the backpacker as a wellspring of transcendent values. We are no longer clear about our own nature, whether we are made in the image of God, or are merely a machine or computer, or animal. These are not

trivial, academic issues. Unless we can make reasonable distinctions between what is natural and what is not, and why that difference is important, we are liable to be at the mercy of the engineers who want to remake all of nature, including our own.

Environmental literacy also requires a broad familiarity with the development of ecological consciousness. The best history of the concept of ecology is Donald Worster's *Nature's Economy*. It is unclear whether the science of ecology will be "the last of the old sciences, or the first of the new." As the former, ecology is the science of efficient resource management. As the first of the new sciences, ecology is the basis for a broader search for pattern and meaning. As such it cannot avoid issues of values, and the ethical questions raised most succinctly in Leopold's "The Land Ethic."

The study of environmental problems is an exercise in despair unless it is regarded as only a preface to the study, design, and implementation of solutions. The concept of sustainability implies a radical change in the institutions and patterns that we have come to accept as normal. It begins with ecology as the basis for the redesign of technology, cities, farms, and educational institutions, and with a change in metaphors from mechanical to organic, industrial to biological. As part of the change we will need alternative measures of well-being such as those proposed by Amory Lovins (least-cost end-use analysis), H. T. Odum (energy accounting), and John Cobb (index of sustainable welfare). Sustainability also implies a different approach to technology, one that gives greater priority to those that are smaller in scale, less environmentally destructive, and rely on the free services of natural systems. Not infrequently, technologies with these characteristics are also highly cost-effective, especially when subsidies for competing technologies are leveled out.

If sustainability represents a minority tradition, it is nonetheless a long one dating back at least to Jefferson. Students should not be considered ecologically literate until they have read Thoreau, Kropotkin, Muir, Albert Howard, Alfred North Whitehead, Gandhi, Schweitzer, Aldo Leopold, Lewis Mumford, Rachel Carson, E. F. Schumacher, and Wendell Berry. There are alternatives to the present patterns that have remained dormant or isolated, not because they did not work, were poorly thought out, or were impractical, but because they were not tried. In contrast to the directions of modern society, this tradition emphasizes democratic participation, the extension of ethical obligations to the land community, careful ecological design, simplicity, widespread competence with natural systems, the sense of place, holism, decentralization of whatever can best be decentralized, and human-scaled technologies and communities. It is a tradition dedicated to the search for patterns, unity, connections between people of all ages, races, nationalities, and generations, and between people and the natural world. This is a tradition grounded in the belief that life is sacred and not to be carelessly expended on the ephemeral. It is a tradition that challenges militarism, injustice, ecological destruction, and authoritarianism, while supporting all of those actions that lead to real peace, fairness, sustainability, and people's right to participate in those decisions that affect their lives. Ultimately, it is a tradition built on a view of ourselves as finite and fallible creatures living in a world limited by natural laws. The contrasting Promethean view, given force by the success of technology, holds that we should remove all limits, whether imposed by nature, human nature, or morality. Its slogan is found emblazoned on the advertisements of the age: "You can have it all" (Michelob Beer), or "Your world should know no limits" (Merrill Lynch). The ecologically literate citizen will recognize these immediately for what they are: the stuff of epitaphs. Ecological literacy leads in other, and more durable, directions toward prudence, stewardship, and the celebration of the Creation.

What Is Education For?

David W. Orr

"The problem" of conservation education, according to Aldo Leopold, "is how to bring about a striving for harmony with land among a people many of whom have forgotten there is such a thing as land." Nearly a half century after those words were written, we know that the problem is more complex and difficult than perhaps Leopold believed. Even in our more ecologically aware age, he would have perceived a sharp decline in the "consciousness of land" and the "striving for harmony" that he regarded as the bedrock of a durable civilization. I think he would also perceive the problem more broadly as "environmental" (not simply "conservation") education, and as more difficult now than he did in 1948.

The problem is in reality many problems, none of which can be separated from larger questions about the purposes, structure, and processes of education at all levels.

Paradigms. First, can the harmony that Leopold proposed be realized within the modern paradigm, which emphasizes human dominance over the natural world, consumption, economic growth, and science and technology, and is organized around nation-states and corporations? Or, as Lynton Caldwell puts it: "What is the significance of man's relationship to his environment, and what implications does the answer hold for present and future human behavior?" Is environmentalism simply another subject or academic department, or is it potentially an integrative principle leading to a radical reconceptualization of education? For those accepting the modern paradigm, environmentalism amounts to little more than fine-tuning a good thing. Environmental education, therefore, can be easily accommodated within existing disciplines and departments. But proponents of a "biospheric" viewpoint and "deep ecologists" advocate much more sweeping changes in the human relationship with the natural world and hence significant changes in education, involving the development of environmental studies as, in Caldwell's term, a "metadiscipline." These proponents are in effect advocating a postmodern paradigm.

The conflict between the two paradigms is not easily resolved, because it concerns alternative views of the proper human role in nature, differences over the potential of science and technology to rescue us from ecological malfeasance, and varying estimates of the malfeasance itself.

Values. Should we strive to teach values appropriate to sustainability, or should we present these as only one possible orientation to the world? Is it possible to treat the work of Julian Simon and economist Nicholas Georgescu-Roegen as if they are equivalent? Is value-free education possible? Is it desirable? If neither, how can values be integrated into the learning process without jeopardizing objectivity and a fair treatment of facts, data, and logic?

As difficult as these issues may be, there are good precedents for the integration of objectivity with a strong value orientation. Medical education, for example, has a clear bias toward human health, not disease. The overriding concern of reputable international relations scholars such as Quincy Wright, Kenneth Boulding, Richard Falk, and Anatol Rapaport is the promotion of peace, not war. Likewise, economics is intended to expand our understanding of the conditions for prosperity. Except by pedants, knowledge has never been regarded as an end in itself, but rather as a means to human well-being. By the same logic, environmental studies ought to have a clear direction favoring harmony between human and natural systems while preserving objectivity in the handling of facts, data, and logic.

Scope and definition of education. The aim of education is often described as teaching people how to think. But think about what? How is this learning to occur? If we strive to educate intelligence alone, which aspects of intelligence do we select? What about other traits, such as character, intuition, feeling, practical abilities, and instincts, which affect what people think about and how well they think? If harmony with nature is important, how is this taught? Can ecologically appropriate values be communicated if students are passive receptors of information in a highly competitive setting? Can one teach about the interrelatedness of biological phenomena without reference to the potential for personal wholeness? Even more basic, can we teach about environmental affairs without also reworking the physical setting of education to favor greater environmental harmony?

Definition of knowledge. These questions lead to others about the definition of knowledge and the way in which research and disciplinary agendas are set. From the perspective of human survival, what is worth knowing? How do we distinguish between the trivial and the important? Implicit in much of our thinking is an assumption that knowledge grows in a neutral, Darwinian fashion in which those ideas best fitted to reality survive, while others less suited do not. This assumption ignores the political, social, and above all, economic influences on the process of paradigm creation and maintenance. For example, the Department of Defense and corporate funding for university research will bias disciplinary agendas, including hiring and tenure decisions, in favor of knowledge useful for certain interests and purposes. Other knowledge or areas of potential knowledge wither, but not because they are less interesting or less important. Alan Schnaiberg has made the same point in documenting the overdevelopment of "production sciences" and the corresponding anemia of the "impact sciences" (meaning those that study the effects of human actions). We might similarly ask why we know so much about chemical-based agribusiness and so little about the means and techniques of sustainable agriculture. Or about manipulative medicine to the exclusion of preventive medicine and nutrition. Or, until recently, about energy production instead of conservation and renewable sources? Why do we spend several hundred billion dollars each year for weapons and preparations to fight wars and a fraction of one percent of that amount on peace research? In each case, the reasons cannot be found in comparative data about efficiency, or ecological impacts, or public morality.

Knowledge, for all pretensions to the contrary, is biased by the way in which we determine social and economic priorities. To respond that science is a self-correcting enterprise through mechanisms of peer review is no answer at all. Science can be directed toward life-enhancing or life-destroying research, each performed with great rigor and dedication.

But how does a society determine priorities in creating and preserving knowledge that accords somehow with ecological realities? If true understanding of ecosystems and the human role in nature require, as I believe it does, development of alternative modes of knowing and perceiving that are integrative, what does this mean? How does one "do" integrative science? How do we perceive holistically?

Structure. What do these questions mean for the structure of the learning environment? Is environmental education and the emergence of integrative science best done in separate departments, or should it be woven throughout the entire curriculum? The case for the latter, including Caldwell's proposal for a metadiscipline, lies in the "logic" of environmentalism, that is, the interaction of life processes. But this logic does not readily clarify priorities, objectives, and curricular details, let alone the transition strategy from the present discipline-centric structure to metadisciplines or whatever else.

The case for confining environmental studies within separate departments, it seems, is best made on grounds of political feasibility, intellectual coherence, and practical manageability. Moreover, it does not exclude the possibility that metadisciplines will emerge eventually through a process of intellectual and institutional maturation. Its danger lies in the possibility, even probability, that environmental studies departments will become just another jealously guarded, closed, academic fiefdom, and will fail to catalyze ecological thinking.

For members of environmental studies programs, what does ecological thinking mean? How do we recognize it in hiring decisions? Few would argue that the process of academic credentialling is without flaws. Yet attainment of a Ph.D. and publication of scholarly research do provide a benchmark to judge individual qualifications. But increasing specialization has substantially narrowed the focus of scholarship. Most active scholars communicate to a small number of colleagues with similar interests through a growing number of highly specialized journals. This system implicitly involves the assumption that bits of information can be integrated by some social-political structure or process or invisible hand into some socially useful and coherent whole. Given the present knowledge explosion, however, we are building a Tower of Babel with each discipline and subdiscipline having its own jargon, theories, and paradigms understood only by a small number of the elect. The social costs of this system are incalculable. The survival issues on the human agenda, which involve whole systems of knowledge and many disciplines, receive little attention. Given the present structure of academia and its hiring, tenuring, and promotion procedures, it is not at all clear how we will identify, debate, research, and ultimately contribute to decisions that lead to farsighted, just, peaceful, and sustainable results.

If questions of environmental education cannot be separated from the broad issues of education, the reverse is equally true: the field of education can no longer afford to ignore two challenges arising from the environmental perspective. The first is the challenge of interrelatedness. We have structured education and the entire knowledge enterprise along Cartesian lines stressing reductionism, discrete entities, linearity, and simple causation, and must now shift to perceive patterns, context, systems, and complex networks of causation that span the sciences, social sciences, and humanities. Further, we must learn to overcome the parochialism inherent in nationality, geography, generation, sex, species, race, and class. If it can be done at all, this revolution in thought, perception, and behavior will go far beyond the Copernican or Darwinian revolutions, whose effects were scarcely felt at the level of daily life, politics, or international affairs.

The second challenge posed by environmentalism concerns the essential misconception of our role in the natural world. For the past five hundred years our sciences, social sciences, and humanities alike have been committed to extending and celebrating the human domination of nature. The idea that we can dominate nature, however, is proving to be both a dangerous and paradoxical illusion. The ecological implications of the philosophy of domination now loom ahead like the icebergs before the *Titanic*. Our civilization is moving at an unprecedented velocity and mass. Any change in this course will require that we rapidly transform values, institutions, and the way we define and transmit knowledge.

We must nonetheless act before the full implications of these two challenges are fully apparent. This process may be roughly analogous to the modern Enlightenment, which reshaped the Western world. We now need an ecological enlightenment which revolutionizes our world and worldviews.

Those presuming to educate should not stand aloof from the decisions about how and whether life will be lived in the twenty-first century. To do so would be to miss the Mount Everest issues on the historical topography of our age, and condemn ourselves to irrelevance. The change I have in mind is not easy to define, but it certainly would include a broad attachment to qualities of health, harmony, balance, diversity, peace, participation, and justice. Such a commitment does nothing to weaken the objectivity with which scholars handle facts and data. To the contrary, the crisis of sustainability has occurred precisely because of flaws, incompleteness, and biases in our data, facts, and logic. The transition to sustainability will require more complete facts, broader sorts of data, a more thorough integrative logic, greater intellectual creativity, and an even deeper commitment to truth.

Environmental education is unavoidably political. At the heart of the issue is the total demand humans make on the biosphere and the way we have organized the flows of energy, water, material, food, and wastes, which in turn affects what political scientists define as the essential issues of politics: "Who gets what, when, and how?" The symptoms of environmental deterioration are in the domain of the natural sciences,

but the causes lie in the realm of the social sciences and humanities. To assume that technology will absolve us from our own folly is only to compound the error. Whatever its many advantages, technology has varying political, social, economic, and ecological implications that we are now only beginning to recognize. Without political, social, and value changes, no technology will make us sustainable. More to the point, do we equip students morally and intellectually to be a part of the existing pattern of corporate-dominated resource flows, or to take part in reshaping these patterns toward greater sustainability? These represent two very different visions of postindustrial society, and two very different orientations to the political realm.

Third, for these reasons, education appropriate for sustainability will give greater emphasis to place-specific knowledge and skills useful in meeting individual local needs, and for rebuilding local communities. The rise of the modern nation-state, corporation, and megalopolis has drained talent, initiative, power, capital, and responsibility from the fine grain of society. The results have been devastating, both ecologically and socially. In the process of becoming a technologically advanced, modern society, as Paul Sears once put it: "We lengthened and elaborated the chain of technology that intervenes between us and the natural world...becom(ing) steadily more vulnerable to even the slightest failure in that chain."

A more socially and ecologically resilient society will create a greater balance between knowledge that can be applied only through large organizations and that which is widely diffused throughout society and meets local needs, culture, and ecology. Professional knowledge can become another restricted commodity for purchase and another way to create incompetence and hence dependence. The relationship between local self-reliance, appropriately scaled technology, societal sustainability, and citizen competence rooted in vernacular traditions is striking. So too are the benefits, including less dependence on foreign suppliers to greater community cohesion and economic resilience.

CONCLUSION

Thomas Kuhn, in his classic *The Structure of Scientific Revolutions*, suggests that scientific knowledge grows in two distinct ways. The first, which he labels "normal science," expands like an ink blot around an accepted paradigm of shared values, methods, rules of evidence, and problems. Knowledge thus grows incrementally as successive generations of scientists are trained in the context of the dominant paradigm and explore its various implications. "Normal science" works well until "anomalies" occur. These may go unrecognized or be purposely ignored, because "no part of the aim of normal science is to call forth new sorts of phenomena; indeed those that will not fit the box are often not seen at all." When this happens, Kuhn suggests, knowledge may grow by a second process in which some scientists deviate from orthodoxy to create an alternative paradigm for solving otherwise insuperable problems. As in the case of Copernicus, Newton, and Einstein, new paradigms lead to a new understanding of the world and constitute what Kuhn describes as "scientific revolutions."

A similar process may be a work in education. The state of the planet represents a series of anomalies for contemporary education. Any adequate response to the emerging agenda of the twenty-first century will require great institutional flexibility, willingness to experiment, funding, and patience. But budget and enrollment problems for many colleges and universities can be expected to further reduce institutional flexibility and the willingness of administrators to tolerate structural chaos and experimentation—let alone to pay for it. Second, for faculty who must continue to keep up with their field, teach, research, publish, and do committee chores, finding time and resources to develop the breadth necessary to comprehend environmental studies is difficult at best. Institutions of higher education are not well structured to encourage renaissance thinking; yet the logic of environmentalism requires no less.

Third, a decent environmental studies program could acquaint students with the major issues—the sciences of ecology and thermodynamics, the social-political–economic-philosophical causes of environmental degradation, and the outlines of sustainable alternatives—and still fail because its graduates were unable to make the leap from "I know" to "I care" to "I'll do something." The first stage results from programmatic thoroughness, the second from a bonding process involving the integration of analytic intelligence, personhood, and experience, and the third from empowered get-up-and-go. Evidence overwhelmingly demonstrates that all three are essential to learning. But not all experience is educationally worthwhile. Carefully designed experiential education which reinforces intellectual and personal growth will require a deeper understanding of what kinds of experience catalyze what kinds of learning. Unfortunately, the typical campus and curriculum offer little opportunity of any sort for experiential learning, whether interaction with nature or the acquisition of competence with life-support systems.

I think the outlines of an alternative paradigm of research and education are emerging from a disparate group of university and college-based environmental studies programs and nontraditional organizations. Like the English ships before the Spanish Armada in 1588, their strength lies in their flexibility, autonomy, vision, and creativity. Despite substantial differences in size, orientation, and purpose, they share common concerns including: (1) ecological sustainability; (2) appropriate scale; (3) cultural and ecological diversity; (4) reevaluation of the goals and directions of industrial society; and (5) justice, peace, and participation. They also share a common intellectual heritage that includes ecologists such as Odum and Sears; systems theorists such as Bertalanffy and Boulding; naturalists such as Krutch and Eiseley; environmental activists such as David Brower; social theorists such as Kropotkin, Kohr, Mumford, and Bateson; and social activists such as Gandhi. Common to all of these organizations is the idea of ecology as an integrative principle and the basis for a marked shift in the perception of the human role in nature, and in the way societies deal with needs for food, energy, water, material, transportation, health care, and waste cycling.

Whatever paths the field of environmental studies follow, we must work, as Leopold observed, against "the fact that our educational and economic system is headed away from...an intense consciousness of land." Accordingly, those of us in environmental education need to renew our commitment to a sustainable human future. The foundation of sustainability, however defined, will be the clear awareness that our well-being is inseparable from that of nature. And, "If education does not teach us these things," Leopold once asked, "then what is education for?"

Four Challenges of Sustainability

David W. Orr

The concept of sustainability first came to public notice in Wes Jackson's work on agriculture in the late 1970s and Lester Brown's *Building a Sustainable Society* and Robert Allen's *How to Save the World* in 1980. The Brundtland Commission made sustainability a central feature of its 1987 report, defining it as meeting the needs of the present generation without compromising the ability of future generations to do the same. Their definition confused sustainable growth, an oxymoron, and sustainable development, a possibility. Ambiguities notwithstanding, the concept of sustainability has become the keystone of the global dialogue about the human future. But what exactly do we intend to sustain and what will that require of us?

Such questions would have had little meaning to generations prior to, say, 1950, when nuclear annihilation became possible. Other than a collision between Earth and a large meteor there was no conceivable way that civilization everywhere could have been radically degraded or terminated. But now any well-informed high-school student could make a long list of ways in which humankind could cause its own demise, ranging from whimpers to bangs. The dialogue about sustainability is about a change in the human trajectory that will require us to rethink old assumptions and engage the large questions of the human condition that some presume to have been solved once and for all.

The things that cannot be sustained are clear. The ongoing militarization of the planet along with the greed and hatred that feeds it are not sustainable. Sooner or later a roll of the dice will come up Armageddon whether in the Indian subcontinent, in the Middle East, or by an accidental nuclear weapons launch or acts of a rogue state or terrorists. A world with a large number of desperately poor cannot be sustained, because they have the power to disrupt the lives of the comfortable in ways that we are only beginning to appreciate and that would not be worth sustaining anyway. The perpetual enlargement of the human estate cannot be sustained because it will eventually overwhelm the capacity and fecundity of natural systems and cycles. The unrestrained development of any and all technology cannot be sustained without courting risks and adverse consequences that we often see only when it is too late. A world of ever-increasing economic, financial, and technological complexity cannot be sustained because sooner or later it will overwhelm our capacity to manage. A world divided by narrow, exclusive, and intense allegiances to ideology or ethnicity cannot be sustained because its people will have too little humor, compassion, forgiveness, and wisdom to save themselves. Unrestrained automobility, hedonism, individualism, and conspicuous consumption cannot be sustained because they take more than they give back. A spiritually impoverished world cannot be sustained because meaninglessness, anomie, and despair will corrode the desire to be sustained and the belief that humanity is worth sustaining. But these are the very things that distinguish the modern age from its predecessors. Genuine sustainability, in other words, will come not from superficial changes but from a deeper process akin to humankind growing up to a fuller stature.

The question, then, is not whether we will change, but whether the transition will be done with more or less grace and whether the destination will be desirable or not. The barriers to a graceful transition to sustainability, whatever forms it may take, are not so much technological as they are social, political, and psychological. It is possible that we will be paralyzed by information overload leading to a kind of psychic numbness. It is possible that we will suffer what Thomas Homer-Dixon calls an "ingenuity gap," in which problems outrun our problem-solving capacities. It is possible that the sheer scale and complexity of human systems will become utterly unfathomable, hence unmanageable. It is possible that we will fail to comprehend the nature of nature sufficiently to know how to live well on the Earth in large numbers. It is possible that we will fail to make a smooth transition because of political ineptitude and a lack of leadership and/or because power is co-opted by corporations and private armies. It is possible that we will fail because powers of denial and wishful thinking cause us to underestimate the magnitude of our problems and to overlook better possibilities. And it is possible that we might fail because of what can only be called a condition of spiritual emptiness. The challenges of sustainability come hard on the heels of a century in which perhaps as many as 200 million people were killed in wars, ethnic conflicts, and extermination camps, taking a psychic toll that we dimly understand.

On the other hand it is possible, and I think likely, that the challenge of survival is precisely what will finally bring humankind together in the realization of the fragility of civilization and the triviality of most of our causes relative to this one central issue. The overall challenge of sustainability is to avoid crossing irreversible thresholds that damage the life systems of Earth while creating long-term economic, political, and moral arrangements that secure the well-being of present and future generations. We will have to acknowledge

that the Enlightenment faith in human reason is, in some measure, wrong. But this does not mean less enlightenment, but rather a more enlightened enlightenment tempered by the recognition of human fallibility—a more rational kind of reason. In this light the great discovery of the modern era is not how to make nuclear fire, or alter our genes, or communicate at the speed of light but, rather, the discovery of our interconnectedness and implicatedness in the web of life. Our challenge is to comprehend what that awareness means in every area of life in order to calibrate human demands with what the Earth can sustain. Broadly speaking, the transition to sustainability poses four challenges.

First, we need more accurate models, metaphors, and measures to describe the human enterprise relative to the biosphere. We need a compass that defines true north for a civilization long on means and short on direction. On the one hand the conventional wisdom describes us as masters of the planet destined to become ever more numerous and rich without explaining how this is possible or why it might be desirable. In contrast, Howard and Elisabeth Odum argue "that many, if not all, of the systems of the planet have common properties, organize in similar ways, have similar oscillations over time, have similar patterns spatially, and operate within universal energy laws." From the perspective of systems ecology, the efflorescence of humanity in the twentieth century is evidence of a natural pulsing. But having exhausted much of the material basis for expansion, like other systems, we are entering a down cycle, a "long process of reorganizing to form a lesser economy on renewable resources" before another upward pulse. The pattern of growth/retreat found by the Odums in all systems stands in marked contrast to the rosy assumptions of perpetual economic growth. So, too, the prescriptions that follow. For the Odums smart policy would include plans for a prosperous descent, to avoid an otherwise catastrophic collapse. The specific tasks they propose are to "stabilize capitalism, protect the Earth's production of real wealth, and develop equity among nations."

Archeologist Joseph Tainter proposes a similar model based on the rise and collapse of complex societies. Collapse eventually occurs when "investment in sociopolitical complexity . . . reaches a point of declining marginal returns." In Tainter's view, this is "not a fall to some primordial chaos, but a return to the normal human condition of lower complexity." Patterns of declining marginal returns, he believes, are now evident in some contemporary industrial societies in areas of agriculture, minerals and energy production, research, health care, education, and military and industrial management. Like the Odums, Tainter regards expansion and contraction as parts of a normal process. But how might we know whether we are in one phase or the other? The answer requires better accounting tools that relate human wealth generation to some larger measure of biophysical wealth. The Odums propose the concept of Emergy or what they define as "the available energy of one kind that has to be used up directly and indirectly to make a product or service." By their accounting, the amount of embodied energy in solar equivalent units gives a more accurate picture of our relative wealth than purely financial measures. Others are developing different tools for the same purpose of including natural capital otherwise left out of purely economic accounting.

Second, the transition to sustainability will require a marked improvement and creativity in the arts of citizenship and governance. There are some things that can be done only by an alert citizenry acting with responsive and democratically controlled governments. Only governments moved by an ethically robust and organized citizenry can act to ensure the fair distribution of wealth within and between generations. Only governments prodded by their citizens can act to limit risks posed by technology or clean up the mess afterward. Only governments and an environmentally literate public can choose to adopt and enforce standards that move us toward a cradle-to-

cradle materials policy. Only governments acting on a public mandate can license corporations and control their activities for the public benefit over the long-term. Only governments can create the financial wherewithal to rebuild ecologically sound cities and dependable public transportation systems. Only governments acting with an informed public can set standards for the use of common property resources including the air, waters, wildlife, and soils. And only governments can implement strategies of resilience that enable the society to withstand unexpected disturbances. Resilience means dispersed, not concentrated, assets, control, and capacity. A resilient society, for instance, would have widely dispersed manufacturing, many small farms, many small cities and towns, greater self-reliance, and few if any technologies vulnerable to catastrophic failure, acts of God, or human malice. Sustainability, in short, constitutes a series of public choices that require effective institutions of governance and a well-informed democratically engaged citizenry.

The third challenge, then, is to inform the public's discretion through greatly improved education. The kind of education needed for the transition to sustainability, however, has little to do with improving SAT or GRE scores or advancing skills necessary to an expansionist phase of human culture. "During growth," write the Odums, "emphasis was on getting new information . . . but as resource availability declines, emphasis [will be] on efficiency in teaching information that we already have." They suggest a curriculum organized around the study of the relationships between energy, environment, and economics and how these apply across various scales of knowledge. Students of all ages will need the kind of education and skills appropriate to building a society with fewer cars but more bicycles and trains; fewer large power plants but more windmills and solar collectors; fewer supermarkets and more farmers' markets; fewer large corporations and more small businesses; less time for leisure but more good work to do; and less public funding but more public spirit.

From the Odums' perspective this is a generation that must foster the regeneration of natural capital of soils, forests, watersheds, and wild areas; clean up the toxic messes from the expansionist phase; restore sustainably habitable cities; relearn the practices of good farming; and learn the arts of powering civilization on efficiency and sunlight. Education appropriate to their future, not least, will require the courage ·to provide "intellectual leadership for the long-run" based on a clear understanding of where we stand relative to larger cycles and trends.

It is easy, however, to offer long lists of solutions and still not solve the larger problem. The difficulty, once identified by E. F. Schumacher, is that human problems, like those posed by the transition to sustainability, are not solvable by rational means alone. These are what he called "divergent" problems, formed out of the tensions between competing perspectives that cannot be solved but can be transcended. In contrast to "convergent" problems that can be solved by logic and method, divergent problems can only be resolved by higher forces of wisdom, love, compassion, understanding, and empathy. The logical mind does not much like divergent problems because it operates more easily with "either/or, or yes/no . . . like a computer." Recognizing the challenge of sustainability as a series of divergent problems leads to the fourth and most difficult challenge of all.

The transition to sustainability will require learning how to recognize and resolve divergent problems, which is to say a higher level of spiritual awareness. By whatever name, something akin to spiritual renewal is the sine qua non of the transition to sustainability. Scientists in a secular culture are often uneasy about matters of spirit, but science on its own can give no reason for sustaining humankind. It can, with equal rigor, create both the knowledge that will cause our demise or that necessary to live at peace with each other and nature. But the spiritual acumen necessary to solve divergent problems posed by the transition to sustainability cannot be just a return to some simplistic religious faith of an earlier time. It must be founded on a higher order of awareness that honors mystery, science, life, and death.

Specifically, the kind of spiritual renewal essential to sustainability must enable us to forgive the terrible wrongs at the heart of the bitter ethnic and national rivalries of past centuries and move on. There is no convergent logic or scientific solution that will enable us to transcend self-perpetuating hatreds and habitual violence. The only solution to this divergent problem is a profound sense of forgiveness and mercy that rises above the convergent logic of justice. The spiritual renewal necessary for the transition must provide convincing grounds by which humankind can justify the project of sustainability. We are, in Lynn Margulis's words, "upright mammalian weeds." But is this all that we are or all that we can be? If so, we have little reason to be sustained beyond the sheer will to live. Perhaps this is enough, but I doubt it.

A robust spiritual sense may not mean that we are created in the image of God, but it must offer hope that we may grow into something more than a planetary plague. A robust spirituality must help us go deeper in order to resolve what Ernest Becker once described as the "terror of death" that "haunts the human animal like nothing else." The effort, to deny the reality of our death, he believed, serves as "a mainspring of human activity" including much that we now see cannot be sustained. "Modern man is drinking and drugging himself out of awareness," he wrote," or he spends his time shopping, which is the same thing. . . . Taking life seriously means that whatever man does on this planet has to be done in the lived truth of the terror of creation, of the grotesque, of the rumble of panic underneath everything." In words written shortly before his own death, Becker concluded that "The urge to cosmic heroism, then, is sacred and mysterious and not to be neatly ordered and rationalized by science and secularism." No culture has gone farther than our own to deny individual mortality, and in the denying is the killing of the planet. A spirituality that allows us to face our own mortality honestly, without denial or terror, contains the seeds of the daily heroism necessary to preserve life on Earth. Instead of terror, a deeper spirituality would lead us to a place of gratitude and celebration.

Love It or Lose It:
The Coming Biophilia Revolution

David W. Orr

*I have set before you life and death, blessing and cursing:
therefore choose life, that both thou and thy seed may live.*
— DEUTERONOMY 30:19

NATURE and I are two," filmmaker Woody Allen once said, and apparently the two have not gotten together yet (Lax, 1992, pp. 39–40). Allen is known to take extraordinary precautions to limit bodily and mental contact with rural flora and fauna. He does not go in natural lakes, for example, because "there are live things in there." The nature Allen does find comfortable is that of New York City, a modest enough standard for wildness.

Allen's aversion to nature, what can be called biophobia, is increasingly common among people raised with television, Walkman radios attached to their heads, and video games and living amidst shopping malls, freeways, and dense urban or suburban settings where nature is permitted tastefully, as decoration. More than ever we dwell in and among our own creations and are increasingly uncomfortable with nature lying beyond our direct control. Biophobia ranges from discomfort in "natural" places to active scorn for whatever is not manmade, managed, or air-conditioned. Biophobia, in short, is the culturally acquired urge to affiliate with technology, human artifacts, and solely with human interests regarding the natural world. I intend the word broadly to include as well those who regard nature "objectively" as nothing more than "resources" to be used any way the favored among the present generation see fit.

Is biophobia a problem as, say, misanthropy or sociopathy, or is it merely a personal preference; one plausible view of nature among many? Is it OK that Woody Allen feels little or no sympathy or kinship with nature? Does it matter that a growing number of other people do not like it or like it only in the abstract as nothing more than resources to be managed or as television nature specials? Does it matter that we are increasingly separated from the conditions of nature? If these things do matter, how do they matter and why? And why have so many come to think that the created world is inadequate? Inadequate to what and for what?

At the other end of the continuum of possible orientation toward nature is "biophilia," which E. O. Wilson (1984) has defined as "the urge to affiliate with other forms of life" (p. 85). Erich Fromm (1973) once defined it more broadly as "the passionate love of life and of all that is alive" (pp. 365–366). Both agree, however, that biophilia is innate and a sign of mental and physical health. To what extent are our biological prospects and our sanity now dependent on our capacity for biophilia? To that degree it is important that we understand how biophilia comes to be, how it prospers, what competencies and abilities it requires of us, and how these are to be learned.

Biophilia is not all that tugs at us. The affinity for life or biophilia competes with other drives and affinities, including biophobia disguised beneath the abstractions and presumptions of progress found in economics, management, and technology. Whatever is in our genes, then, the affinity for life is now a choice we must make. Compared with earlier cultures, our distinction lies in the fact that technology now allows us to move much further toward total domination of nature than ever before. Serious and well-funded people talk about reweaving the fabric of life on earth through genetic engineering and nanotechnologies, others talk of leaving the earth altogether for space colonies, and still others talk of reshaping human consciousness to fit "virtual reality." If we are to preserve a world in which biophilia can be expressed and can flourish, we will have to decide to make such a world.

❖ The Origins and Consequences of Biophobia ❖

In varying degrees humans have always modified their environments. I am persuaded that they generally have intended to do so with decorum and courtesy toward nature—not always and everywhere to be sure, but mostly. On balance, the evidence further suggests that biophilia or something close to it was woven throughout the myths, religions, and mindset of early humankind, which saw itself as participating with nature. In Owen Barfield's words, people once felt "integrated or mortised into" the world in ways that we do not and perhaps cannot (Barfield, 1957, p. 78). Technology, primitive by our standards, set limits on what tribal cultures could do to the world, while their myths, superstitions, and taboos constrained what they thought they ought to do. But I do not think that early humans *chose* biophilia, if for no other reason than that there was no choice to be made. And those tribes and cultures that were biophobic or incompetent toward nature passed into oblivion through starvation and disease (Diamond, 1992, pp. 317–338).

Looking back across that divide, I think it is evident that tribal cultures possessed an ecological innocence of sorts because they did not have the possibilities or the knowledge given to us. We, in contrast, must choose between biophobia and biophilia because science and technology have given us the power to destroy so completely as well as the knowledge to understand the consequences of doing so. The divide was not a sharp break but a kind of slow tectonic shift in perception and attitudes that widened throughout the late Middle Ages to the present. What we call "modernization" represented dramatic changes in how we regard the natural world and our role in it. These changes are now so thoroughly ingrained in us that we can scarcely conceive of any other manner of thinking. But crossing this divide first required us to discard the belief that the world was alive and worthy of respect, if not fear. To dead matter, we owe no obligations. Second, it was necessary to distance ourselves from animals who were transformed by Cartesian alchemy into mere machines. Again, no obligations or pity are owed to machines. In both cases, use is limited only by usefulness. Third, it was necessary to quiet whatever remaining sympathy we had for nature in favor of "hard" data that could be weighed, measured, counted, and counted on to make a profit. Fourth, we needed a reason to join power, cash, and knowledge in order to transform the world into more useful forms. Francis Bacon provided the logic, and the evolution of government-funded research did the rest. Fifth, we required a philosophy of improvement and found it in the ideology of perpetual economic growth, now the central mission of governments everywhere. Sixth, biophobia required the sophisticated cultivation of dissatisfaction, which could be converted into mass consumption. The advertising industry and the annual style change were invented.

For these revolutions to work, it was necessary that nature be rendered into abstractions and production statistics of board feet, tons, barrels, and yield. It was also necessary to undermine community, especially the small community, where attachment to place might grow and with it resistance to crossing the divide. Finally it was necessary to convert politics into the pursuit of material self-interest and hence render people impotent as citizens and unable to talk of larger and more important things.

To this point the story is well known, but it is hardly finished. Genetic engineers are busy remaking the fabric of life on earth. The development of nanotechnologies—machines at the molecular level—create possibilities for good and evil that defy prediction. How long will it be until the genetic engineers or nanotechnologists release an AIDS-like virus? One can only guess. But even those promoting such technologies admit that they "carry us toward unprecedented dangers . . . more potent than nuclear weapons" (Drexler, 1987, p. 174). And immediately ahead is the transformation of human consciousness brought on by the conjunction of neuroscience and computers in machines that will simulate whatever reality we choose. What happens to the quality of human experience or to our politics when cheap and thoroughgoing fantasy governs our mental life? In each case, untransformed nature pales by comparison. It is clumsy, inconvenient, flawed, and difficult to move or rearrange. It is slow. And it cannot be converted to mass dependence and profits so easily.

Beneath each of these endeavors lies a barely concealed contempt for unaltered life and nature, as well as contempt for the people who are expected to endure the mistakes, purchase the results, and live with the consequences, whatever those may be. It is a contempt disguised by terms of bamboozlement, like *bottom line*, *progress*, *needs*, *costs and benefits*, *economic growth*, *jobs*, *realism*, *research*, and *knowledge*, words that go undefined and unexamined. Few people, I suspect, believe "in their bones" that the net results from all of this will be positive, but most feel powerless to stop what seems to be so inevitable and unable to speak what is so hard to say in the language of self-interest.

The manifestation of biophobia, explicit in the urge to control nature, has led to a world in which it is becoming easier to be biophobic. Undefiled nature is being replaced by a defiled nature of landfills, junkyards, strip mines, clear-cuts, blighted cities, six-lane freeways, suburban sprawl, polluted rivers, and superfund sites, all of which deserve our phobias. Ozone depletion, meaning more eye cataracts and skin cancer, does give more reason to stay indoors. The spread of toxic substances and radioactivity does mean more disease. The disruption of natural cycles and the introduction of exotic species has destroyed much of the natural diversity that formerly graced our landscapes. Introduced blights and pests have or are destroying American chestnuts, elms, maples, dogwoods, hemlocks, and ashes. Global warming will degrade the flora and fauna of familiar places (Peters and Myers, 1991–1992, pp. 66–72). Biophobia sets into motion a vicious cycle that tends to cause people to act in such a way as to undermine the integrity, beauty, and harmony of nature, creating the very conditions that make the dislike of nature yet more probable.

Even so, is it OK that Woody Allen, or anyone else, does not like nature? Is biophobia merely one among a number of equally legitimate ways to relate to nature? I do not think so. First, for every "biophobe" others have to do that much more of the work of preserving, caring for, and loving the nature that supports biophobes and biophiliacs alike. Economists call this the "free-rider problem." It arises in every group, committee, or alliance when it is possible for some to receive all of the advantages of membership while doing none of the work necessary to create those advantages. Environmental free riders benefit from others' willingness to fight for the clean air that they breathe, the clean water that they drink, the preservation of biological diversity that sustains them, and the conservation of the soil that feeds them. But they lift not a finger. Biophobia is not OK because it does not distribute fairly the work of keeping the earth or any local place.

Biophobia is not OK for the same reason that misanthropy and sociopathy are not OK. We recognize these as the result of deformed childhoods that create unloving and often violent adults. Biophobia in all of its forms similarly shrinks the range of experiences and joys in life in the same way that the inability to achieve close and loving relationships limits a human life. E. O. Wilson (1984) put it this way:

> People can grow up with the outward appearance of normality in an environment largely stripped of plants and animals, in the same way that passable looking monkeys can be raised in laboratory cages and cattle fattened in feeding bins. Asked if they were happy, these people would probably say yes. Yet something vitally important would be missing, not merely the knowledge and pleasure that can be imagined and might have been, but a wide array of experiences that the human brain is peculiarly equipped to receive. (p. 118)

Can the same be said of whole societies that distance themselves from animals, trees, landscapes, mountains, and rivers? Is mass biophobia a kind of collective madness? In time I think we will come to know that it is.

Biophobia is not OK because it is the foundation for a politics of domination and exploitation. For our politics to work as they now do, a large number of people must not like any nature that cannot be repackaged and sold back to them. They must be ecologically illiterate and ecologically incompetent, and they must believe that this is not only inevitable but desirable. Furthermore, they must be ignorant of the basis of their dependency. They must come to see their bondage as freedom and their discontents as commercially solvable problems. The drift toward a biophobic society, as George Orwell and C. S. Lewis foresaw decades ago, requires the replacement of nature and human nature by technology and the replacement of real democracy by a technological tyranny now looming on the horizon.

These are reasons of self-interest: It is to our advantage to distribute the world's work fairly, to build a society in which lives can be lived fully, and to create an economy in which people participate knowledgeably. There is a further argument against biophobia that rests not on our self-interest, but on our duties. Finally, biophobia is not OK because it violates an ancient charge to replenish the earth. In return for our proper use, the earth is given to humankind as a trust. Proper use requires gratitude, humility, charity, and skill. Improper use begins with ingratitude and disparagement and proceeds to greed, abuse, and violence. We cannot forsake the duties of stewardship without breaking another trust with those who preceded us and with those who will follow.

Biophobia is certainly more complex than I have described it. One can be both biophobic and a dues-paying member of the Sierra Club. It is possible to be nature averse but still "like" the idea of nature as an abstraction. Moreover, it is possible to adopt the language and guise of biophilia and do a great deal of harm to the earth, knowingly or unknowingly. In other words, it is possible for us to be inconsistent, hypocritical, and ignorant of what we do.

But is it possible for us to be neutral or "objective" toward life and nature? I do not think so. On closer examination, what often passes for neutrality is nothing of the sort but rather the thinly disguised self-interest of those with much to gain financially or professionally. For those presuming to wear the robes of objectivity, the guise, as Abraham Maslow's

(1966) words, is often "a defense against being flooded by the emotions of humility, reverence, mystery, wonder, and awe" (p. 139). Life ought to excite our passion, not our indifference. Life in jeopardy ought to cause us to take a stand, not retreat into a spurious neutrality. Furthermore, it is a mistake to assume that commitment precludes the ability to think clearly and to use evidence accurately. To the contrary, commitment motivates intellectual clarity, integrity, and depth. We understand this in other realms quite well. When the chips are down, we do not go to physicians who admit to being neutral about the life and death of their patients. Nor when our hide is at stake do we go to lawyers who profess "objective" neutrality between justice and injustice. It is a mistake to think that matters of environment and life on earth are somehow different. They are not, and we cannot in such things remain aloof or indifferent without opening the world to demons.

❖ Biophilia ❖

We relate to the environment around us in different ways, with differing intensity, and these bonds have different sources. At the most common level, we learn to love what has become familiar. There are prisoners who prefer their jail cell to freedom; city dwellers, like Woody Allen, who shun rural landscapes or wilderness; and rural folk who will not set foot in the city. Simply put, we tend to bond with what we know well. Geographer Yi-Fu Tuan (1974) described this bonding as "topophilia," which includes "all of the human being's affective ties with the material environment" (p. 93). Topophilia is rooted less in our deep psychology than it is in our particular circumstances and experiences. It is closer to a sense of habitat that is formed out of the familiar circumstances of everyday living than it is a genuine rootedness in the biology and topography of a particular place. It is not innate, but acquired. New Yorkers have perhaps a greater sense of topophilia or habitat than do residents of Montana. But Montanans are more likely to feel kinship with sky, mountains, and trout streams. Both, however, tend to be comfortable with what has become habitual and familiar.

E. O. Wilson (1984) suggested a deeper source of attachment that goes beyond the particularities of habitat. "We are," he argues, "a biological species [that] will find little ultimate meaning apart from the remainder of life" (p. 112). We are bound to living things by what Wilson described as an innate urge to affiliate, or "biophilia," which begins in

early childhood and "cascades" into cultural and social patterns. Biophilia is inscribed in the brain itself, expressing tens of thousands of years of evolutionary experience. It is evident in our preference for landscapes that replicate the savannas on which mind evolved: "Given a completely free choice, people gravitate statistically toward a savanna-like environment" (Wilson, 1984, p. 115). Removed to purely artificial environments and deprived of "beauty and mystery," the mind "will drift to simpler and cruder configurations," which undermine sanity itself (Wilson, 1984, p. 118). Still, biophilia competes with what Wilson describes as the "audaciously destructive tendencies of our species" that seem also to have "archaic biological origins" (p. 121). Allowing these tendencies free rein to destroy the world "in which the brain was assembled over millions of years" is, Wilson has argued, "a risky step."

A third possibility is that at some level of alertness and maturity, we respond with awe to the natural world independent of any instinctual conditioning. "If you study life deeply," Albert Schweitzer (1969) once wrote, "its profundity will seize you suddenly with dizziness" (p. 115). He described this response as "reverence for life" arising from the awareness of the unfathomable mystery of life itself. (The German word Schweitzer used, *Ehrfurcht*, implies greater awe than is implied by the English word *reverence*.) Reverence for life, I think, is akin to what Rachel Carson (1965/1987) meant by "the sense of wonder." But for Schweitzer (1972) reverence for life originated in large measure from the intellectual contemplation of the world: "Let a man once begin to think about the mystery of his life and the links which connect him with the life that fills the world, and he cannot but bring to bear upon his own life and all other life that comes within his reach the principle of Reverence for Life" (p. 231). Schweitzer regarded reverence for life as the only possible basis for a philosophy on which civilization might be restored from the decay he saw throughout the modern world. "We must," he wrote, "strive together to attain to a theory of the universe affirmative of the world and of life" (Schweitzer, 1972, p. 64).

We have reason to believe that this intellectual striving is aided by what is already innate in us and may be evident in other creatures. No less an authority than Charles Darwin believed that "all animals feel wonder" (Darwin, 1977, p. 450). Primatologist Harold Bauer once observed a chimpanzee lost in contemplation by a spectacular waterfall in the Gombe Forest Reserve in Tanzania. Contemplation finally gave way to "pant-hoot" calls while the chimp ran back and forth drumming on trees with its fists (Konner, 1982, p. 431). No one can say for certain what this behavior means, but it is not farfetched to see it as a chimpanzee version of awe and ecstasy. Jane Goodall and others have described similar behavior. It would be the worst kind of anthropocentrism to dismiss such accounts in the belief that the capacity for biophilia and awe is a human monopoly. In fact it may be that we have to work at it harder than other creatures. Joseph Wood Krutch (1991), for one, believed that for birds and other creatures "joy seems to be more important and more accessible than it is to us" (p. 227). And not a few philosophers have agreed with Abraham Heschel (1990) that "as civilization advances, the sense of wonder almost necessarily declines" (p. 37).

Do we, with all of our technology, retain a built-in affinity for nature? I think so, but I know of no proof that would satisfy skeptics. If we do have such an innate sense, we might nevertheless conclude from the damage that we have done to the world that biophilia does not operate everywhere and at all times. It may be, as Erich Fromm (1973) argued, that biophilia can be dammed up or corrupted and can subsequently appear in other, more destructive forms:

> Destructiveness is not parallel to, but the alternative to biophilia. Love of life or love of the dead is the fundamental alternative that confronts every human being. Necrophilia grows as the development of biophilia is stunted. Man is biologically endowed with the capacity for biophilia, but psychologically he has the potential for necrophilia as an alternative solution. (p. 366)

We also have reason to believe that people can lose the sense of biophilia. For example, in his autobiography, Darwin (1958) admitted that "fine scenery . . . does not cause me the exquisite delight which it formerly did" (p. 54). It is also possible that entire societies can lose the capacity for love of any kind. When the Ik tribe in northern Uganda was forcibly moved from its traditional hunting grounds into a tiny reserve, their world, as Colin Turnbull (1972) expressed it, "became something cruel and hostile," and they "lost whatever love they might once have had for their mountain world" (pp. 256, 259). The love for their place the Ik people may have once felt was transmuted into boredom and a "moody distrust" of the world around them and matched by social relations that Turnbull described as utterly loveless, cruel, and despicable. The Ik are a

stark warning to us that the ties to life and to each other are more fragile than some suppose and, once broken, are not easily repaired or perhaps cannot be repaired at all.

Much of the history of the twentieth century offers further evidence of the fragility of biophilia and of philia. Ours is a time of unparalleled human violence and unparalleled violence toward nature. This is the century of Auschwitz and the mass extinction of species, nuclear weapons, and exploding economic growth.

Even if we could find no evidence of a lingering human affinity or affection for nature, however, humankind is now in the paradoxical position of having to learn altruism and selflessness, but for reasons of survival that are reasons of self-interest. In the words of Stephen Jay Gould (1991), "We cannot win this battle to save species and environments without forging an emotional bond between ourselves and nature as well— for we will not fight to save what we do not love" (p. 14). And if we do not save species and environments, we cannot save ourselves; we depend on those species and environments in more ways than we can possibly know. We have, in other words, "purely rational reasons" to cultivate biophilia (Wilson, 1984, p. 140).

Beyond our physical survival, there is still more at risk. The same Faustian urges that drive the ecological crisis also erode those qualities of heart and mind that constitute the essence of our humanity. Bertrand Russell (1959) put it this way:

> It is only in so far as we renounce the world as its lovers that we can conquer it as its technicians. But this division in the soul is fatal to what is best in man. . . . The power conferred by science as a technique is only obtainable by something analogous to the worship of Satan, that is to say, by the renunciation of love. . . . The scientific society in its pure form . . . is incompatible with the pursuit of truth, with love, with art, with spontaneous delight, with every ideal that men have hitherto cherished. (p. 264)

The ecological crisis, in short, is about what it means to be human. And if natural diversity is the wellspring of human intelligence, then the systematic destruction of nature inherent in contemporary technology and economics is a war against the very sources of mind. We have good reason to believe that human intelligence could not have evolved in a lunar landscape, devoid of biological diversity. We also have good reason to believe that the sense of awe toward the creation had a great deal to do with the origin of language and that early hominids *wanted* to talk, sing, and write poetry in the first place. Elemental things like flowing water, wind, trees, clouds, rain, mist, mountains, landscape, animals, changing seasons, the night sky, and the mysteries of the life cycle gave birth to thought and language. They continue to do so, but perhaps less exuberantly than they once did. For this reason I think it not possible to unravel natural diversity without undermining human intelligence as well. Can we save the world and anything like a human self from the violence we have unleashed without biophilia and reverence for the creation? All the arguments made by technological fundamentalists and by the zealots of instrumental rationality notwithstanding, I know of no good evidence that we can. We must choose, in Joseph Wood Krutch's (1991) words, whether "we want a civilization that will move toward some more intimate relation with the natural world or . . . one that will continue to detach and isolate itself from both a dependence upon and a sympathy with that community of which we were originally a part?" (p. 165). The writer of Deuteronomy had it right. Whatever our feelings, however ingenious our philosophies, whatever innate gravity tugs at us, we must finally choose between life and death, between intimacy and isolation.

❖ Biophilia: Eros to Agape ❖

We are now engaged in a great global debate about what it means to live "sustainably" on the earth. This word, however, is fraught with confusion, in large part because we are trying to define it before we have decided whether we want an intimate relation with nature or total mastery, as Krutch (1991) put it. We cannot know what sustainability means until we have decided what we intend to sustain and how we propose to do so. For some, sustainability means maintaining our present path of domination, only with greater efficiency. But were we to decide, in concurrence with Krutch and others, that we do want an intimate relation with nature, to take nature as our standard, what does that mean? We must choose along the continuum that runs between biophilia and biophobia and between intimacy and mastery, but how can we know when we have crossed over from one to the other? The choices are not always so simple, nor will they be presented to us so candidly. The options, even the most destructive, will be framed as life-serving, as necessary for a greater good someday, or as simply inevitable since "you can't stop progress." How, then, can we distinguish those things that serve life broadly and well from those that diminish it?

Biophilia is a kind of philia or love, but what kind? The Greeks distinguished three kinds of love: *eros*, meaning love of beauty or romantic love aiming to possess; *agape*, or sacrificial love, which asks nothing in return; and *philia*, or the love between friends. The first two of these reveal important parts of biophilia, which probably begins as eros but matures, if at all, as a form of agape. For the Greeks eros went beyond sensuous love to include creature needs for food, warmth, and shelter, as well as higher needs to understand, appreciate, and commune with nature (Bratton, 1992, p. 11). But eros aims no higher than self-fulfillment. Defined as an "innate urge," biophilia is eros, reflecting human desire and self-interest, including the interest in survival.

Biophilia as eros, however, traps us in a paradox. According to Susan Bratton (1992), "Without agape, human love for nature will always be dominated by unrestrained eros and distorted by extreme self-interest and material valuation" (p. 15). What we love only from self-interest, we will sooner or later destroy. Agape tempers our use of nature so that "God's providence is respectfully received and insatiable desire doesn't attempt to extract more from creation than it can sustain" (Bratton, 1992, p. 13). Agape enlarges eros, bringing humans and the creation together so that it is not possible to love either humanity or nature without also loving and serving the other. Agape in this sense is close to Schweitzer's description of "reverence for life," which calls us to transcend even the most enlightened calculations of self-interest. Wouldn't respect for nature do as well? I think not, and for the reason that it is just too bloodless, too cool, and too self-satisfied and aloof to cause us to do much to save species and environments. I am inclined to agree with Stephen Jay Gould that we will have to reach deeper.

What, then, do we know about deeper sources of motivation, including the ways in which eros is transformed into agape, and what does this reveal about biophilia? First, we know that the capacity for love of any kind begins early in the life and imagination of the child. The potential for biophilia possibly begins at birth, as Robert Coles once surmised, with the newborn infant being introduced to its place in nature (Coles, 1971). If so, the manner and circumstances of birth are more important than is usually thought. Biophilia is certainly evident in the small child's efforts to establish intimacy with the earth, like that of Jane Goodall, age two, sleeping with earthworms under her pillow (Montgomery, 1991, p. 28), or John Muir (1988), "reveling in the wonderful wildness" around his boyhood Wisconsin home (p. 43). If by some fairly young age, however, nature has not been experienced as a friendly place of adventure and excitement, biophilia will not take hold as it might have. An opportunity will have passed, and thereafter the mind will lack some critical dimension of perception and imagination.

Second, I think we know that biophilia requires easily and safely accessible places where it might take root and grow. For Aldo Leopold it began in the marshes and woods along the Mississippi River. For young E. O. ("Snake") Wilson (1984) it began in boyhood explorations of the "woods and swamps in a languorous mood . . . [forming] the habit of quietude and concentration" (pp. 86–92). The loss of places such as these is one of the uncounted costs of economic growth and urban sprawl. It is also a powerful argument for containing that sprawl and expanding urban parks and recreation areas.

Third, I think we can safely surmise that biophilia, like the capacity to love, needs the help and active participation of parents, grandparents, teachers, and other caring adults. Rachel Carson's (1987) relation with her young nephew caused her to conclude that the development of a child's sense of wonder required "the companionship of at least one adult who can share it, rediscovering with him the joy, excitement and mystery of the world we live in" (p. 45). For children the sense of biophilia needs instruction, example, and validation by a caring adult. And for adults, rekindling the sense of wonder may require a child's excitement and openness to natural wonders as well.

Fourth, we have every reason to believe that love and biophilia alike flourish mostly in good communitites. I do not mean necessarily affluent places. In fact, affluence often works against real community, as surely as does violence and utter poverty. By community I mean, rather, places in which the bonds between people and those between people and the natural world create a pattern of connectedness, responsibility, and mutual need. Real communities foster dignity, competence, participation, and opportunities for good work. And good communities provide places in which children's imagination and earthy sensibilities root and grow.

Fifth, we have it on good authority that love is patient, kind, enduring, hopeful, long-suffering, and truthful, not envious, boastful, insistent, arrogant, rude, self-centered, irritable, and resentful (I Corinthians 13).

For biophilia to work, I think it must have similar qualities. Theologian James Nash (1991) for example proposed six ecological dimensions of love: (1) beneficence, e.g., kindness to wild creatures; (2) other-esteem, which rejects the idea of possessing or managing the biosphere; (3) receptivity to nature, e.g., awe; (4) humility, by which is meant caution in the use of technology; (5) knowledge of ecology and how nature works; and (6) communion as "reconciliation, harmony, koinonia, shalom" between humankind and nature (pp. 139–161). I would add only that real love does not do desperate things, and it does not commit the irrevocable.

Sixth, I think we know with certainty that beyond some scale and level of complexity, the possibility for love of any sort declines. Beneficence, awe, reconciliation, and communion are not entirely probable attitudes for the poverty stricken living in overcrowded barrios. With 10 or 12 billion people on the earth, we will have no choice but to try to manage nature, even though it will be done badly. The desperate and the hungry will not be particularly cautious with risky technologies. Nor will the wealthy, fed and supplied by vast, complex global networks, understand the damage they cause in distant places they never see and the harm they do to people they will never know. Knowledge has its own limits of scale. Beyond some level of scale and complexity, the effects of technology, used in a world we cannot fully comprehend, are simply unknowable. When the genetic engineers and the nanotechnologists finally cause damage to the earth comparable to that done by the chemists who invented and so casually and carelessly deployed chlorofluorocarbons, they too will plead for forgiveness on the grounds that they did not know what they were doing.

Seventh, love, as Eric Fromm (1989) wrote, is an art, the practice of which requires "discipline, concentration and patience throughout every phase of life" (p. 100). The art of biophilia, similarly, requires us to use the world with disciplined, concentrated, and patient competence. To live and earn our livelihood means that we must "daily break the body and shed the blood of creation," in Wendell Berry's (1981) words. Our choice is whether we do so "knowingly, lovingly, skillfully, reverently . . . [or] ignorantly, greedily, clumsily, destructively" (p. 281). Practice of any art also requires forbearance, which means the ability to say no to things that diminish the object of love or our capacity to work artfully. And for the same reasons that it limits the exploitation of persons, forbearance sets limits on our use of nature.

Finally, we know that for love to grow from eros to agape, something like *metanoia*, or the "transformation of one's whole being" is necessary. Metanoia is more than a "paradigm change." It is a change, first, in our loyalties, affections, and basic character, which subsequently changes our intellectual priorities and paradigms. For whole societies, the emergence of biophilia as agape will require something like a metanoia that deepens our loyalty and affections to life and over time alters the character of our entire civilization.

THE BIOPHILIA REVOLUTION

"Is it possible," E. O. Wilson (1984) asked, "that humanity will love life enough to save it?" (p. 145). And if we do love life enough to save it, what is required of us? On one level the answer is obvious. We need to transform how and how rapidly we use the earth's endowment of land, minerals, water, air, wildlife, and fuels: an efficiency revolution that buys us some time. Beyond efficiency, we need another revolution that transforms our ideas of what it means to live decently and how little is actually necessary for a decent life: a sufficiency revolution. The first revolution is mostly about technology and economics. The second revolution is about morality and human purposes. The biophilia revolution is about the combination of reverence for life and purely rational calculation by which we will *want* to both be efficient and live sufficiently. It is about finding our rightful place on earth and in the community of life, and it is about citizenship, duties, obligations, and celebration.

There are two formidable barriers standing in our way. The first is the problem of denial. We have not yet faced up to the magnitude of the trap we have created for ourselves. We are still thinking of the crisis as a set of problems that are, by definition, solvable with technology and money. In fact we face a series of dilemmas that can be avoided only through wisdom and a higher and more comprehensive level of rationality than we have yet shown. Better technology would certainly help; however, our crisis is not fundamentally one of technology but one of mind, will, and spirit. Denial must be met by something like a worldwide ecological "perestroika," predicated on the admission of failure: the failure of our economics, which became disconnected from life; the failure of our politics, which lost sight of the moral roots of our commonwealth; the failure of our science, which lost sight of the essential wholeness of things; and the failures of all of us as moral beings, who allowed these things to happen because we did not love deeply and intelligently enough. The biophilia

revolution must come as an ecological enlightenment that sweeps out the modern superstition that we are knowledgeable enough and good enough to manage the earth and to direct evolution.

The second barrier standing in the way of the biophilia revolution is one of imagination. It is easier, perhaps, to overcome denial than it is to envision a biophilia-centered world and believe ourselves capable of creating it. We could get an immediate and overwhelming worldwide consensus today on the proposition "Is the world in serious trouble?" But we are not within a light-year of agreement on what to do about it. Confronted by the future, the mind has a tendency to wallow. For this reason we can diagnose our plight with laser precision while proposing to shape the future with a sledgehammer. Fictional utopias, almost without exception, are utterly dull and unconvincing. And the efforts to create utopias of either right or left have been monumental failures, leaving people profoundly discouraged about their ability to shape the world in accord with their highest values. And now some talk about creating a world that is sustainable, just, and peaceful! What is to be done?

Part of our difficulty in confronting the future is that we think of utopia on too grand a scale. We are not very good at comprehending things on the scale of whole societies, much less that of the planet. Nor have we been very good at solving the problems utopias are supposed to solve without imposing simplistic formulas that ride roughshod over natural and cultural diversity. Except for some anarchists, utopianism is almost synonymous with homogenization. Another part of the problem is the modern mind's desire for drama, excitement, and sexual sizzle, which explains why we do not have many bestselling novels about Amish society, arguably the closest thing to a sustainable society we know. How do we fulfill the need for meaning and variety while discarding some of our most cherished fantasies of domination? How do we cause the "change in our intellectual emphasis, loyalties, affections, and convictions," without which all else is moot? (Leopold, 1966, p. 246) When we think of revolution, our first impulse is to think of some grand political, economic, or technological change; some way to fix quickly what ails us. What ails us, however, is closer to home, and I suggest that we begin there.

THE RECOVERY OF CHILDHOOD: I began by describing biophilia as a choice. In fact it is a series of choices, the first of which has to do with the conduct of childhood and how the child's imagination is woven into a home place. Practically, the cultivation of biophilia calls for the establishment of more natural places, places of mystery and adventure where children can roam, explore, and imagine. This means more urban parks, more greenways, more farms, more river trails, and wiser land use everywhere. It means redesigning schools and campuses to replicate natural systems and functions. It means greater contact with nature during the school day but also unsupervised hours to play in places where nature has been protected or allowed to recover.

For biophilia to take root, we must take our children seriously enough to preserve their natural childhood. However, childhood is being impoverished and abbreviated, and the reasons sound like a curriculum in social pathology: too many broken homes and unloving marriages, too much domestic violence, too much alcohol, too many drugs, too many guns, too many things, too much television, too much idle time and permissiveness, too many off-duty parents, and too little contact with grandparents. Children are rushed into adulthood too soon, only to become childish adults unprepared for parenthood, and the cycle repeats itself. We will not enter this new kingdom of sustainability until we allow our children the kind of childhood in which biophilia can put down roots.

RECOVERING A SENSE OF PLACE: I do not know whether it is possible to love the planet or not, but I do know that it is possible to love the places we can see, touch, smell, and experience. And I believe, along with Simone Weil (1971), that rootedness in a place is "the most important and least recognized need of the human soul" (p. 43). The attempt to encourage biophilia will not amount to much if we fail to decide to reshape these kinds of places so that we might become deeply rooted. The second decision we must make, then, has to do with the will to rediscover and reinhabit our places and regions, finding in them sources of food, livelihood, energy, healing, recreation, and celebration. Whether one calls it "bioregionalism" or "becoming native to our places" it means deciding to relearn the arts that Jaquetta Hawkes (1951) once described as "a patient and increasingly skillful love-making that [persuades] the land to flourish" (p. 202). It means rebuilding family farms, rural villages, towns, communities, and urban neighborhoods. It means restoring local culture and our ties to local places, where biophilia first takes root. It means reweaving the local ecology into the fabric of the economy and life patterns while diminishing use of the automobile and our ties to the commercial culture. It means deciding to slow down, hence more bike trails, more gardens, and more solar collectors. It means rediscovering and restoring the nat-

ural history of our places. And, as Gary Snyder (1974) wrote, it means finding our place and digging in (p. 101).

EDUCATION AND BIOPHILIA: The capacity for biophilia can still be snuffed out by education that aims no higher than to enhance the potential for upward mobility, which has come to mean putting as much distance as possible between the apogee of one's career trajectory and one's roots. We should worry a good bit less about whether our progeny will be able to compete as a "world-class workforce" and a great deal more about whether they will know how to live sustainably on the earth. My third proposal, then, requires the will to reshape education in a way that fosters innate biophilia and the analytical abilities and practical skills necessary for a world that takes life seriously.

Lewis Mumford (1946) once proposed the local community and region as the "backbone of a drastically revised method of study" (pp. 150–154). The study of the region would ground education in the particularities of a specific place and would also integrate various disciplines around the "regional survey," which includes surveys of local soils, climate, vegetation, history, economy, and society. Mumford (1970b) envisioned this as an "organic approach to knowledge" that began with the "common whole—a region, its activities, its people, its configuration, its total life" (p. 385). The aim was "to educate citizens, to give them the tools of action" and to educate a people "who will know in detail where they live and how they live . . . united by a common feeling for their landscape, their literature and language, their local ways" (Mumford, 1970b, p. 386).

Something like the regional survey is required for the biophilia revolution. Education that supports and nourishes a reverence for life would occur more often out-of-doors and in relation to the local community. It would provide a basic competence in the kinds of knowledge that Mumford described a half century ago. It would help people become not only literate but ecologically literate, understanding the biological requisites of human life on earth. It would provide basic competence in what I have called the "ecological design arts," that is, the set of perceptual and analytic abilities, ecological wisdom and practical wherewithal essential to making things that fit in a world governed by the laws of ecology and thermodynamics.

A NEW COVENANT WITH ANIMALS: The biophilia revolution would be incomplete without our creating a new relationship with animals, one, in Barry Lopez's (1989) words, that "rise(s) above prejudice to a position of respectful regard toward everything that is different from ourselves and not innately evil" (p. 383). We need animals, not locked up in zoos, but living free on their own terms. We need them for what they can tell us about ourselves and about the world. We need them for our imagination and for our sanity. We need animals for what they can teach us about courtesy and what Gary Snyder (1990) called "the etiquette of the wild" (pp. 3–24). The human capacity for biophilia as agape will remain "ego-centric and partial" until it can also embrace creatures who cannot reciprocate (Mumford 1970a, p. 286). And needing animals, we will need to restore wild landscapes that invite them again.

A new covenant with animals requires that we decide to limit the human domain in order to establish their rights in law, custom, and daily habit. The first step is to discard the idea obtained from Rene Descartes that animals are only machines, incapable of feeling pain and to be used any way we see fit. Protecting animals in the wild while permitting confinement feeding operations and most laboratory use of animals makes no moral sense and diminishes our capacity for biophilia. In this, I think Paul Shepard (1993) is right: To recognize animals and wildness is to decide to admit deeper layers of our consciousness into the sunlight of full consciousness again.

THE ECONOMICS OF BIOPHILIA: The biophilia revolution will also require national and global decisions that permit life-centeredness to flourish at a local scale. Biophilia can be suffocated, for example, by the demands of an economy oriented toward accumulation, speed, sensation, and death. But economists have not written much about how an economy encourages or discourages love generally or biophilia in particular. As a result, not much thought has been given to the relationship between love and the way we earn our keep.

The transition to an economy that fosters biophilia requires a decision to limit the human enterprise relative to the biosphere. Some economists talk confidently of a five- or tenfold increase in economic activity over the next half century. But Peter Vitousek and his colleagues have shown that humans now use or coopt 40% of the net primary productivity from terrestrial ecosystems (Vitousek et al., 1986). What limits does biophilia set on the extent of the human enterprise? What margin of error does love require?

Similarly, in the emerging global economy, in which capital, technology, and information move easily around the world, how do we protect the people and the communities left behind? Now more than ever the rights of capital are protected by all the power money can buy. The rights of communities are protected less than ever. Consequently, we face complex decisions about how to protect communities and their stability on which biophilia depends.

BIOPHILIA AND PATRIOTISM: The decisions necessary to move us toward a culture capable of biophilia are, in the end, political decisions. But our politics, no less than our economy, has other priorities. In the name of "national security" or one ephemeral national "interest" or another we lay waste to our lands and to the prospects of our children. Politics of the worst sort has corrupted our highest values, becoming instead one long evasion of duties and obligations in the search for private or sectarian advantage. "Crackpot realists" tell us that this is how it has always been and must therefore always be: a view that marries bad history to bad morals.

Patriotism, the name we give to the love of one's country, must be redefined to include those things that contribute to the real health, beauty, and ecological stability of our home places and to exclude those that do not. Patriotism as biophilia requires that we decide to rejoin the idea of love of one's country to how and how well one uses the country. To destroy forests, soils, natural beauty, and wildlife in order to swell the gross national product, or to provide short-term and often spurious jobs, is not patriotism but greed.

Real patriotism requires that we weave the competent, patient, and disciplined love of our land into our political life and our political institutions. The laws of ecology and those of thermodynamics, which mostly have to do with limits, must become the foundation for a new politics. No one has expressed this more clearly than Vaclav Havel (1989): "We must draw our standards from our natural world. . . . We must honour with the humility of the wise the bounds of that natural world and the mystery which lies beyond them, admitting that there is something in the order of being which evidently exceeds all our competence" (p. 153). Elsewhere, Havel (1992) stated the following:

> Genuine Politics . . . is simply a matter of serving those around us: serving the community, and serving those who will come after us. Its deepest roots are moral because it is a responsibility, expressed through action, to and for the whole, a responsibility . . . only because it has a metaphysical grounding: that is, it grows out of a

conscious or subconscious certainty that our death ends nothing, because everything is forever being recorded and evaluated somewhere else, somewhere 'above us', in what I have called 'the memory of being'. . . . (p. 6)

❖ Conclusion ❖

Erich Fromm (1955) once asked whether whole societies might be judged sane or insane. After the World Wars, state-sponsored genocide, gulags, McCarthyism, and the "mutual assured destruction" of the twentieth century there can be no doubt that the answer is affirmative. Nor do I doubt that our descendants will regard our obsession with perpetual economic growth and frivolous consumption as evidence of theologically induced derangement. Our modern ideas about sanity, in large measure, can be attributed to Sigmund Freud, an urban man. And from the urban male point of view, the relationship between nature and sanity may be difficult to see and even more difficult to feel. Freud's reconnaissance of the mind stopped too soon. Had he gone further, and had he been prepared to see it, he might have discovered what Theodore Roszak (1992) called "the ecological unconscious," the repression of which "is the deepest root of collusive madness in industrial society" (p. 320). He may also have stumbled upon biophilia, and had he done so, our understanding of individual and collective sanity would have been on more solid ground.

The human mind is a product of the Pleistocene Age, shaped by wildness that has all but disappeared. If we complete the destruction of nature, we will have succeeded in cutting ourselves off from the source of sanity itself. Hermetically sealed amidst our creations and bereft of those of The Creation, the world then will reflect only the demented image of the mind imprisoned within itself. Can the mind doting upon itself and its creations be sane? Thoreau never would have thought so, nor should we.

A sane civilization that loved more fully and intelligently would have more parks and fewer shopping malls; more small farms and fewer agribusinesses; more prosperous small towns and smaller cities; more solar collectors and fewer strip mines; more bicycle trails and fewer freeways; more trains and fewer cars; more celebration and less hurry; more property owners and fewer millionaires and billionaires; more readers and fewer television watchers; more shopkeepers and fewer multinational corporations; more teachers and fewer lawyers; more wilderness and fewer landfills; more wild animals and fewer pets. Utopia? No! In our present circumstances this is the only realistic course imaginable. We have tried utopia and can no longer afford it.

SOURCES

Barfield, O. 1957. *Saving the Appearances*. New York: Harcourt Brace Jovanovich.

Berry, W. 1981. *The Gift of Good Land*. San Francisco: North Point Press.

Bratton, S. 1992, Spring. Loving Nature: Eros or Agape? *Environmental Ethics* 14, 1.

Carson, R. 1987. *The Sense of Wonder*. New York: Harper. (Original work published 1965.)

Coles, R. 1971. A Domain of Sorts. In S. Kaplan and R. Kaplan, eds., *Humanscape*. North Scituate, Mass.: Duxbury.

Darwin, C. 1958. *The Autobiography of Charles Darwin*. New York: Dover. (Original work published 1892.)

Darwin, C. 1977. *The Descent of Man*. New York: Modern Library. (Original work published 1871.)

Diamond, J. 1992. *The Third Chimpanzee*. New York: Harper.

Drexler, E. 1987. *Engines of Creation*. New York: Anchor Books.

Fromm, E. 1955. *The Sane Society*. New York: Fawcett Books.

Fromm, E. 1973. *The Anatomy of Human Destructiveness*. New York: Holt, Rinehart & Winston.

Fromm, E. 1989. *The Art of Loving*. New York: Harper.

Gould, S. 1991, September. Enchanted Evening. *Natural History*, p. 14.

Havel, V. 1989. *Living in Truth*. London: Faber & Faber.

Havel, V. 1992. *Summer Meditations*. New York: Knopf.

Hawkes, J. 1951. *A Land*. New York: Random House.

Heschel, A. 1990. *Man is not Alone*. New York: Farrar, Straus & Giroux.

Konner, M. 1982. *The Tangled Wing*. New York: Holt, Rinehart & Winston.

Krutch, J. 1991. *The Great Chain of Life*. Boston: Houghton Mifflin.

Lax, E. 1992. *Woody Allen: A Biography*. New York: Vintage.

Leopold, A. 1966. *A Sand County Almanac*. New York: Ballantine. (Original work published 1949.)

Lopez, B. 1989. Renegotiating the Contracts. In T. Lyon, ed., *This Incomperable Lande*. Boston: Houghton Mifflin.

Maslow, A. 1966. *The Psychology of Science*. Chicago: Gateway.

Montgomery, S. 1991. *Walking with the Great Apes*. Boston: Houghton Mifflin.

Muir, J. 1988. *The Story of My Boyhood and Youth*. San Francisco: Sierra Club.

Mumford, L. 1946. *Values for Survival*. New York: Harcourt and Brace.

Mumford, L. 1970a. *The Conduct of Life*. New York: Harcourt Brace Jovanovich.

Mumford, L. 1970b. *The Culture of Cities*. New York: Harcourt Brace Jovanovich.

Nash, J. 1991. *Loving Nature*. Nashville: Abingdon.

Peters, R., and Myers, J. P. 1991–1992. Preserving Biodiversity in a Changing Climate. *Issues in Science and Technology,* 8, 2.

Roszak, T. 1992. *The Voice of the Earth.* New York: Simon & Schuster.

Russell, B. 1959. *The Scientific Outlook.* New York: Norton.

Schweitzer, A. 1969. *Reverence for Life.* New York: Pilgrim Press.

Schweitzer, A. 1972. *Out of My Life and Thought.* New York: Holt, Rinehart & Winston.

Shepard, P. 1993. On Animal Friends. In S. Kellert and E. O. Wilson, eds., *The Biophilia Hypothesis.* Washington, DC: Island Press.

Shepard, P., and Sanders, B. 1992. *The Sacred Paw.* New York: Viking.

Snyder, G. 1974. *Turtle Island.* New York: New Directions.

Snyder, G. 1990. *The Practice of the Wild.* San Francisco: North Point Press.

Tuan, Y. 1974. *Topophilia.* New York: Columbia University Press.

Turnbull, C. 1972. *The Mountain People.* New York: Simon & Schuster.

Vitousek, P., et al. 1986, June. Human Appropriation of the Products of Photosynthesis. *Bioscience,* 36, 6.

Weil, S. 1971. *The Need for Roots.* New York: Harper.

Wilson, E. O. 1984. *Biophilia.* Cambridge: Harvard University Press.

Religion and the Quest for a Sustainable World

Gary Gardner

As the U.S. debate over drilling for oil in Alaska's Arctic National Wildlife Refuge (ANWR) gathered steam in early 2002, an unusual ad appeared on television. Over magnificent shots of seacoasts, forests, and mountains, the narrator intones a Jewish prayer in which God is saying, "This is a beautiful world I have given you. Take care of it; do not ruin it." The ad then argues against drilling in ANWR and proposes that the United States' energy needs be met through conservation, higher fuel efficiency standards, and greater use of solar and wind power. Perhaps the most arresting statement is the last one: "Brought to you by the Sierra Club and the National Council of Churches."

The teaming of a prominent U.S. environmental organization and a coalition of mainstream Christian churches is especially surprising because environmentalists and people of faith have had limited connection since the start of the modern environmental movement. Nevertheless, such alignments may represent an emerging trend. Spiritual traditions—from large, centralized religions to local tribal spiritual authorities—are beginning to devote energy to what some see as the defining challenge of our age: the need to build just and environmentally healthy societies.

In this endeavor, religious institutions and leaders can bring at least five strong assets to the effort to build a sustainable world: the capacity to shape cosmologies (worldviews), moral authority, a large base of adherents, significant material resources, and community-building capability. Many political movements would welcome any of these five assets. To be endowed with most or all of them, as many religions are, is to hold considerable political power.

Looking at the first of these assets, we see that religious cosmologies regarding the natural environment are diverse, and the broad range of teachings might suggest that some religions are naturally "greener" than others. But the reality is more complex. Nearly all religions can be commended and criticized for one aspect or another of their posture toward the environment. A religion's environmental credentials may depend on whether its teaching, its practice, or its potential for "greening" itself is being assessed. And scholars see great potential for developing environmental ethics even within traditions that have lacked them.

Growing out of religion's capacity to shape worldview is the capacity to inspire and wield moral authority. Asked in 1935 if the pope might prove to be an ally of the Soviet Union, Josef Stalin is said to have replied scornfully, "The pope? How many divisions has he got?" But papal influence exercised through the Solidarity protest movement in Poland in the early 1980s was an important factor in the eventual unraveling of communist rule in Eastern Europe. Similarly, the Dalai Lama, even though he has lived in exile since 1959, strongly affects Chinese government policy toward Tibet. Charisma and moral suasion are not the exclusive reserve of religious leaders, of course, but religious leaders have extensive experience in these matters.

Turning to the more worldly assets, a third source of power for religions is the sheer number of followers they claim. Although only estimates are available, it seems that over 80 percent of people on the planet belong to one of the world's 10,000 or so religions, with 150 or so of these having at least a million followers each. Adherents of the three largest—Christianity, Islam, and Hinduism—account for about two-thirds of the global population today. Another 20 percent of the world subscribes to the remaining faith traditions. About 15 percent of people are nonreligious.

Degrees of adherence among the billions of religious people vary greatly, of course, as does the readiness of adherents to translate their faith into political action or lifestyle choices. And many believers within the same religion or denomination may interpret their faith in conflicting ways, leading them to act at cross purposes. But the raw numbers are so impressive that mobilizing even a fraction of adherents to the cause of building a just and environmentally healthy society could advance the sustainability agenda dramatically.

Influence stemming from having a large number of followers is further enhanced by the geographic concentration of many religions, which increases their ability to make mass appeals and to coordinate action. In 120 countries, for example, Christians comprise the majority of the population. Muslims are the majority in forty-five countries, and Buddhists dominate in nine. When most people in a society have similar worldviews, leaders can make mass appeals using a single, values-laden language.

The fourth asset many religions can bring to the effort is substantial physical and financial resources. Real estate holdings alone are impressive. The Alliance of Religions and Conservation (ARC), a non-governmental organization based in the United Kingdom, estimates that religions own up to 7 percent of the habitable area of the world. And buildings abound: Pakistan has one mosque for every thirty households; the United States has one house of worship for every 900 residents. In addition, clinics, schools, orphanages, and other religiously run social institutions give religious organizations a network of opportunities to shape development efforts.

While headlines regularly expose the less than ethical use of religious wealth, some exemplary cases illustrate the impact that religious institutions could have in helping to nudge the world toward sustainability. In the United States, the Interfaith Center for Corporate Responsibility (ICCR), representing 275 Protestant, Catholic, and Jewish institutional investors, has been a leader for more than three decades in shaping corporate operating policies through the use of social policy shareholder resolutions. More than half of all socially oriented shareholder resolutions filed in the United States in the past three years were filed or co-filed by religious groups; on more than a third of them, religious groups were the primary filers. This role has caught the attention of secular activists on corporate responsibility. "One of the first things we do when we run a campaign is make sure that the ICCR is on board," says Tracey Rembert of the Shareholder Action Network, which advocates ethical investing and shareholder action.

Finally, religion has a particular capacity to generate social capital: the bonds of trust, communication, cooperation, and information dissemination that create strong communities. Development economists began to recognize in the 1970s and 1980s that economic development is fueled not just by stocks of land, labor, and financial capital but also by education (human capital) and healthy ecosystems (ecological capital). By the 1990s many theorists added social capital (community building) to the list because of its importance as a lubricant and glue in many communities: it greases the wheels of communication and interaction, which in turn strengthens the bonds that community members have with one another.

Data from the United States support the interpretation of religion as community builder. Analyzing survey data, sociologist Andrew Greeley showed that religious institutions or persons, which are responsible for 34 percent of all volunteerism in the United States, generated volunteers not just for religious work but for other society-building efforts as well. About a third of the educational, political, youth, and human services voluntarism, about a quarter of the health-related voluntarism, and about a fifth of the employment-related volunteer work was undertaken by people motivated by their faith. The willingness to work for societal betterment, not just for the particular interests of a religious group, holds potential for the movement to build a sustainable world, especially because the environment is an issue of common concern for the planet and for future generations that transcends religious and national differences.

As deforestation, climate change, water shortages, extensive poverty, and other global ills have assumed greater prominence in the public mind, and as the religious and environmental communities increasingly appreciate their common interest in combating these problems, the two communities have begun to work together on the agenda of sustainable development. And the pace of meetings and collaborations among religious and environmental groups has increased markedly since the World Wide Fund for Nature (WWF) sponsored an interreligious meeting in Assisi, Italy, in 1986 that brought together representatives of five of the world's major religions. That germinal meeting was followed by other major conferences and important initiatives, both between the two communities and among religious traditions. Some of the initiatives have blossomed into networks: for example, the National Religious Partnership for the Environment in the United States and the Alliance for Religions and Conservation in the United Kingdom bring together diverse faith groups to plan strategies for raising awareness and taking action on environmental issues. The increased activity and commitment represented by the initiatives suggests that environmentalism is not just a passing fad for religious groups.

One development of particular note was a ten-part conference series on world religions and ecology held at Harvard University's Center for the Study of World Religions from 1996 to 1998. The series brought together the most diverse spectrum of individuals and institutions ever convened on the topic, with more than 800 scholars and environmental activists from major religious traditions and from six continents participating. The conferences are noteworthy not only for the scholarship they produced—nine volumes on environmentalism from the perspective of major religious traditions, with another forthcoming—but also for their extensive engagement of people from outside of religion and religious studies. Scientists, ethicists, educators, and public policymakers all took an active part. Perhaps most significant for the religion/environment dialogue, the Forum on Religion and Ecology (the follow-on organization to the conferences) is housed at Harvard's Center for the Environment so that scholars of religious traditions can be in continuing contact with environmental scientists and policymakers.

But despite these many laudable advances, serious obstacles remain to more extensive religious/environmental collaboration. They fall into two major categories: mutual misperceptions and differences in worldview that produce opposing positions on sensitive issues.

Today's misperceptions of religion by environmentalists, and of the environmental movement by people of faith, are manifestations of the centuries-long growing chasm between science and spirituality. A landmark 1967 essay by historian Lynn White may have helped widen the breach, at least between groups in the United States. White argued that the Judeo-Christian mandate to subdue the Earth and to be fruitful and multiply set the philosophical foundation for environmentally destructive industrial development in the Christian West. The claim is controversial and has been strongly critiqued by many religious scholars, not least because White's argument is founded on just a few lines of scripture. Still, many critics of White acknowledge that parts of the Bible may have helped create a functional and implemental view of nature among Jews and Christians.

Sierra Club Executive Director Carl Pope takes the critique of White in a different direction, arguing that an entire generation of environmentalists was soured on religion by their skewed reading of White's essay. He notes that environmentalists have widely ignored the fact that, whatever the merits of the critique, White also asserted that religion would need to be part of the solution to the growing environmental crisis. The incomplete reading of White's essay, Pope argues, gave many environmentalists the belief that religion is the problem and led many environmental groups to shun religious communities in their work. He sees this as a great mistake.

At the same time, some negative perceptions of religion aren't entirely unfounded, and these pose special challenges to religious institutions and people of faith. To the extent that religion acts as a conservative social force, it may correctly be perceived as an obstacle to sustainability, since a sustainable world won't be built without major changes to the world's economies. Where religions neglect their prophetic potential and their calling to be critics of immoral social and environmental realities, they are likely to be distrusted by those working to change those trends. Indeed, some would argue that religions and religious people today too seldom wear the mantle of the prophet in the sense of being a critic of the established order. Franciscan writer and author Richard Rohr asks, "Why is it that church people by and large mirror the larger population on almost all counts? . . . On the whole, we tend to be just as protective of power, prestige, and possessions as everyone else."

But Rohr doesn't despair. He sees a long tradition of reform of religion that allows it to get back to its roots—and to the power and influence found there. Paradoxically, that charismatic power emerges from an embrace of powerlessness, vulnerability, and spiritual freedom (liberation from undue attachment to the material world) that are found at the core of the great religions.

Beyond the differences in perception lie tensions that emerge from differing worldviews. Consider the issue of the status of women. Advocates of sustainability often view women as being denied equality and even oppressed by some religions, while some religions see the question of gender equality as a nonissue, given their view that family and societal roles played by men and women are naturally different. Because of the central role of women in combating malnutrition, reducing infectious disease, promoting education, and stabilizing populations, the perception that religion contributes to the marginalization of half of humanity is a serious obstacle for collaboration on development issues. On the other hand, the fact that women are more involved than men in nearly all religions offers hope that their voices will one day carry equal weight with those of men.

Similarly, divergent views of when human personhood begins—at conception, or later—have left many religious people and sustainability advocates at odds over abortion, an especially sensitive issue. Representatives of the Vatican and of Muslim countries, for example, battled with proponents of reproductive rights over language to be included in the final declaration from the International Conference on Population and Development in Cairo, Egypt, in 1994—a battle that left each side more wary than ever about prospects for future dialogue, much less cooperation. As long as the two communities hold their current positions, cooperation is unlikely on those issues.

The profound issue of what constitutes truth is another difference in worldview that can separate the two communities. Some religious positions are based on a belief that the universe contains a set of objective truths—things that are true in all places, at all times—such as that God

exists, or that all sentient beings have a right to live. For many people of faith, objective truth is not negotiable. When the two communities are separated by an issue that religious people see as containing an objective truth, compromise would seem to be impossible. On such issues, the two sides may simply need to agree to disagree, respecting each other's views while putting disagreements aside and working together on areas of agreement.

In addition, different perspectives on the place of humanity in the natural order can also separate the two communities and create divisions within them. Some deep ecologists, for example, see humans as one of many species in the natural world, with no greater or lesser moral value than other species, while more mainstream environmentalists would assign a special place to humanity, even as they demand that humans live in a way that respects the entire natural world. Similar divisions can be found among spiritually inclined people as well, with some spiritual adherents to the Gaia hypothesis—the idea that the planet is a single, interconnected organism, all of which is vital—taking positions similar to those of deep ecologists.

Despite the tremendous challenges, collaboration is possible, even between science-oriented environmentalists and scripturally centered religious traditions. Evangelical Christians in the United States, for example, have formed an Evangelical Environmental Network to promote conservation and environmental stewardship—not only because of scientific arguments for conservation but because they see the natural world as God's creation that must therefore be protected. The group is credited with playing a pivotal role in blocking attempts in the U.S. Congress in 1996 to weaken the Endangered Species Act, calling it the "Noah's Ark of our day" for its role in preserving species, and accusing Congress of "trying to sink it." The credibility of the evangelical group with moderate members of Congress—combined with a $1 million lobbying effort—helped persuade some of those members not to dilute the act.

Consider also the many statements in recent years by religious leaders on behalf of the environment. The Dalai Lama has made environmental protection the theme of numerous major statements since the mid-1980s—including several speeches at the Earth Summit in 1992—and environmental protection is one of the five points of his peace plan for Tibet. Ecumenical Patriarch Bartholomew, symbolic leader of the 250-million-member Orthodox Church, has been in the forefront of bringing scientists and religious leaders together to study water-related environmental issues. And Pope John Paul II issued major environmental statements in 1990 and 2001 and a joint statement with Patriarch Bartholomew in June 2002.

Religions have long had a strong interest in restraining consumption, although for reasons very different from the concerns of environmentalists. The ecological argument against excessive consumption—that population growth, ever-greater levels of individual consumption, and one-time use of materials have combined to deplete stocks of raw materials and to degrade ecosystems—is solid, well established, and stands strongly on its own. But religious traditions broaden the discussion by citing the corrosive effect of excessive consumption not only on the environment but on the development of character, both of individuals and of societies. Living simply, many religions teach, frees resources for those in need and frees the human spirit to cultivate relationships with neighbors, with the natural world, and with the world of spirit. Adding these social and spiritual arguments for moderation to the newer ecological one yields a powerful case for simplicity and situates consumption more clearly in a comprehensive understanding of what it means to be a developed person and a developed society.

Despite a history of teachings on the spiritual corruption associated with excessive attachment to wealth or material accumulation and the issuing of occasional statements on the topic, religious leaders and institutions in industrial nations have largely failed to address the consumerist engine that drives industrial economies. There are few concrete initiatives to promote simple living—such as simplicity circles in pockets of the United States and Europe, where neighbors gather to discuss how to achieve simplicity in a high-consumption culture—and most aren't promoted or sponsored by organized religion. The newly installed Archbishop of Canterbury, Rowan

Williams, has said that curbing the culture of consumption will be a large focus of his ministry as head of the Anglican Church. But he must be sobered by the experience of Pope John Paul II, who set as a strategic goal of his papacy a dampening of the influence of consumerism in industrial cultures. Despite centuries of experience preaching against the illusion of satisfaction provided by earthly wealth, religion in industrial countries is struggling in its efforts to counter the consumerist tide.

These traditions might find encouragement in the spiritually-rooted ethic of moderate consumption found in the developing country, Sri Lanka. Since 1958, a grassroots development effort there known as Sarvodaya Shramadana has promoted village-based development programs that explicitly integrate material and spiritual development. The movement, whose name roughly means "awakening of all through sharing," motivates villagers to undertake a broad range of development projects—from latrine building to establishment of preschools and cultural centers—within a framework of Buddhist principles. The movement has grown to encompass more than half of the country's 24,000 villages and is now the largest development NGO in Sri Lanka. Its success draws on two major assets that religion brings to development: the motivational power of religious principles and the ability to generate and use "social capital" for development.

A creative example in the United States is the work of the Regeneration Project in California, an initiative of the Episcopal Church. It includes Episcopal Power and Light (EP&L), a ministry that promotes green energy and energy efficiency. EP&L was started in 1996 when Reverend Sally Bingham realized that she might capitalize on the state's deregulation of energy to persuade a bloc of customers—the state's Episcopalians—to choose energy generated from renewable sources, such as wind, geothermal, and biomass. The project also encourages participating parishes to undertake an energy audit of their buildings. The Regeneration Project also includes California Interfaith Power and Light, which does political advocacy to promote renewable energy. In its short life, the Regeneration Project has spread to seven states, and it could have a substantial effect on energy consumption patterns if adopted by religious groups and adherents nationwide.

There is more that could be done. By reading the "signs of the times" through the lens of their own scriptures, religious traditions might demonstrate the relevance of their teachings for the major issues of our day, even as they help address the tremendous environmental and social needs of this moment in history. Several tools—retrieval, reevaluation, and reconstruction—are used by some theologians for evaluating scripture and tradition in the light of contemporary circumstances.

Retrieving teachings that have lain dormant but that are especially relevant today has already been discussed. But religions can also reevaluate and reconstruct traditional teachings in light of present realities. A good example of this comes from Africa, where the high rates of HIV infection have pushed some churches and mosques to rethink their teachings on condom use. Increasingly uncomfortable with prohibitions of condom use as they watch masses of people— often their own congregants—lie sick and dying from a disease that prophylactics could largely prevent, many local leaders have questioned religious policies against their use. Muslim communities in several African nations have changed direction on teachings about condoms. And a Catholic bishop in South Africa has called for a reversal of his church's teaching on condom use.

Whether these particular reevaluations and reconstructions should be adopted broadly by various religions is a question to be decided by each tradition. The point here is simply that established religions have centuries of experience reading their central tenets in the light of contemporary realities. Some scholars even suggest replacing the term *religious traditions* with *religious processes*, so consistent is the theme of adaptation in the history of most religions.

The challenge for environmentalists and other advocates of sustainability, meanwhile, may be to build a greater appreciation for the importance of spirituality. All development activities are embedded in a cultural context; if pursued unwisely, they can provoke a cultural backlash. The shah of Iran, in his attempt to "modernize" that country between the 1950s and 1970s, paid too little attention to religious sensibilities in the process and learned firsthand, through the 1979 revolution that dethroned him, how costly this insensitivity can be.

A good demonstration of the sensitivity needed is found at the United Nations Population Fund (UNFPA), which works around the world on issues of reproductive health. In Kenya, where UNFPA seeks to prevent the spread of AIDS by halting the contraction of HIV among sex workers, the agency collaborates with both Catholic parishes and secular health clinics—but in different ways. UNFPA underwrites the provision of condoms at the health clinic. But at the parishes, the agency follows a policy sensitive to Catholic teaching about condom use and funds programs that offer income-generating projects as an alternative to the sex work. In sum, UNFPA identifies common ground for collaboration rather than focusing on areas of difference—a helpful model for traversing the bumpy spots in the relationship between sustainability groups and some religious communities.

In addition to respecting the religious sensibilities of a culture, environmentalists might seek ways to express spirituality in their own programs and communication efforts. Such expressions need not be religious, of course, but might instead focus on creating an emotional/spiritual connection between the public and the natural environment—an indispensable and largely missing link in the effort to generate commitment to sustainability. As the late Harvard biologist and outspoken humanist Stephen Jay Gould suggested, "We cannot win this battle to save species and environments without forging an emotional bond between ourselves and nature as well—for we will not fight to save what we do not love."

Building on Gould's thought, environmental educator David Orr challenges scientists (including environmentalists) to knead emotion into their work. He notes that most biologists and ecologists "believe that cold rationality, fearless objectivity, and a bit of technology" will get humanity out of its environmental predicament. But those tools have long been used with minimal success. What is missing, Orr unabashedly asserts, is love. "Why is it so hard to talk about love, the most powerful of human emotions, in relation to science, the most powerful and far-reaching of human activities?" He notes that passion and good science, far from being antithetical, are as interdependent as the heart and the brain. Both are needed if we are to fully understand our world and our role in it.

Gary Gardner is director of research for the Worldwatch Institute. This article, with the permission of the Worldwatch Institute, is adapted and abridged from chapter eight, "Engaging Religion in the Quest for a Sustainable World," in State of the World 2003: A Worldwatch Institute Report on Progress Toward a Sustainable Society, *published in January 2003 by W. W. Norton and Company.*